... when you need it in writing! ™

FAMILY RECORD

ORGANIZER

Over 200 ready-to-use forms to simply, efficiently and completely organize every aspect of your life.

compiled and edited by
Rhonda R. Porter

E·Z LEGAL FORMS®

Deerfield Beach, Florida 33442

... when you need it in writing! ®

E-Z Legal Forms, Inc.
384 S. Military Trail
Deerfield Beach FL 33442

Distributed by E-Z Legal Forms, Inc.

Manufactured in the United States of America

1 2 3 4 5 6 7 8 9 10

This book is sold with the understanding that neither the author nor the publisher is engaged in rendering legal advice. If legal advice is required, the services of an attorney should be sought. Publisher and author cannot in any way guarantee that the forms in this book are being used for the purposes intended and, therefore, assume no responsibility for their proper and correct use.

Library of Congress Catalog Card Number: 94-070241

Family Record Organizer
  Compiled and edited by Rhonda Porter
      p.   cm.
  ISBN 1-56382-303-9: $24.95
I. Porter Rhonda, compiled and edited by. II. Title: Family Record Organizer

IMPORTANT FACTS

E-Z Legal Products are designed to provide authoritative and accurate information in regard to the subject matter covered. However, neither this nor any other publication can take the place of an attorney on important legal matters.

Information in this book has been carefully compiled from sources believed to be reliable, but the accuracy of the information is not guaranteed, as laws and regulations may change or be subject to differing interpretations.

Why not have your attorney review this book? We encourage it.

LIMITED WARRANTY AND DISCLAIMER

As with any legal matter, common sense should determine whether you need the assistance of an attorney. We urge you to consult with an attorney whenever substantial amounts of money are involved or on any matter when you do not understand how to properly complete a form or question its adequacy to protect you.

It is understood that by using this legal book you are acting as your own attorney. Accordingly, the publisher, author and retailer shall have neither liability nor responsibility to any party for any loss or damage caused or alleged to be caused by use of this book. This book is sold with the understanding that the publisher, author and retailer are not engaged in rendering legal services. If legal services or other expert assistance are required, the services of a competent professional should be sought.

E-Z Legal Forms offers you a limited guarantee. If you consider E-Z Legal Forms to be defective in any way you may return your purchase to us within 30 days for a full refund of the list or purchase price, whichever is lower. In no event shall our liability—or the liability of any retailer—exceed the purchase price of the product. Use of the product constitutes acceptance of these terms.

PRINTED IN THE UNITED STATES OF AMERICA

E-Z LEGAL FORMS
384 S. Military Trail
Deerfield Beach, FL 33442
Tel. 305-480-8933   Fax 305-480-8906

ABOUT
FAMILY RECORD ORGANIZER

Now you can organize your personal life as efficiently as you can your business life with the help of E-Z Legal Forms' Family Record Organizer.

More than 200 forms have been assembled into a comprehensive recordkeeping system called Family Record Organizer, designed to simplify your and your family's lives. This basic, easy-to-use book contains virtually every form you will ever need to keep your life running smoothly, from travel planning to family event scheduling to monthly goal setting.

Family Record Organizer is the ultimate record-maintenance system, designed to locate and organize vital financial, personal, legal, family and household information quickly and conveniently. This book helps you create a permanent record of vital data that encompasses every aspect of your life, and is easy to maintain and update. The forms it contains are easy to understand, ready to use, flexible, and suited to your individual and family needs.

There are a number of ways Family Record Organizer will prove valuable to you. It can help eliminate time-consuming record searching, help you maintain important personal and family records, give you the tools essential for effective planning, and assist you in managing your finances.

Family Record Organizer is divided into eleven sections, each designed to help organize a certain aspect of your life:

Section 1   Family/Personal Records contains forms to help organize everything from your grocery list to your babysitting expenses to your volunteer record.

Section 2   Business Forms assists you in organizing your personal business activities through forms such as a long distance phone call record, home office product order form and advertising budget.

Section 3   Educational Records tracks your scholastic achievements from grade school years through educational courses taken beyond college.

Section 4   Health Records compiles all health care-related documents, including doctor visits and health insurance policies.

Section 5   Investments/Financial Records helps organize your personal finances by compiling all your financial records, from certificates of deposit to zero coupon bonds.

Section 6   Purchase and Maintenance Records helps you keep track of products ordered and products to order. Other forms organize home and vehicle maintenance records.

Section 7   Important Names, Dates and Facts never lets you forget another birthday or anniversary. Important names, events and phone numbers are easily accessible when you complete these forms.

Section 8   Event Planning assists you in organizing your next social gathering. Plan your next Christmas party or special dinner with the help of these forms.

Section 9   Travel Data covers all the travel information you'll need to plan and prepare upcoming business or social trips.

Section 10   Recreational Activities compiles forms to keep records of your hobbies or special interests.

Section 11   Special Projects makes it easier to accomplish your goals by listing objectives and updating project ideas.

Using the forms provided in all eleven sections will lead you to become more organized and efficient in all areas of your life.

Let Family Record Organizer become a part of your daily routine and establish a more organized lifestyle for you and your family.

HOW TO USE
FAMILY RECORD ORGANIZER

You can easily and conveniently use Family Record Organizer by following these simple steps.

1. To find the appropriate form, check the Table of Contents, which lists forms alphabetically by section. The index also lists all forms.

2. You may find several forms for the same general purpose, so carefully review and select the form most appropriate for your specific needs.

3. Each form is perforated for easy removal and use. Photocopy and store the original so it can be used again and again.

4. Fully complete each form, making certain all blanks are filled in.

5. Keep your Family Record Organizer in a safe, convenient place for easy access.

6. Encourage family members to utilize this new system. It can prove to be a valuable and important tool for the entire family.

7. Begin your record keeping process by organizing and categorizing your existing records to correspond with the categorized forms. Prioritizing will simplify the transferral of information into your Family Record Organizer.

8. Weed out inactive or outdated files in order to start your record keeping system with fresh information. (Remember, though, to save inactive records for at least seven years.)

9. Correlate your record keeping system with the records of your accountant, attorney and others to best tailor your system to your professional needs.

10. Take the initiative to personalize and modify the forms in your Family Record Organizer. They can even be used to develop a computerized record keeping system, using E-Z Legal's Family Record Organizer Software.

11. Simplify record keeping by delegating specific record keeping responsibilities to individual family members.

12. Add complementary and convenient record keeping aids or resources offered by associations, banks, investment firms and other companies to your already-comprehensive Family Record Organizer.

13. Where needed, maintain additional copies of essential information at your workplace, vacation home or other secondary locations.

14. Keep confidential information, such as medical or financial information, separate. At least one other person, however, should know where to locate this information.

15. Assure the availability of your records by avoiding storage places such as safe deposit boxes, which are often sealed upon death.

16. Back up written Organizer records with supplemental records. For example, entries in the "Vehicle Service Log" should be accompanied by copies of invoices from the service stations that performed the work on your vehicle.

17. Update your Family Record Organizer on an as-needed basis. The best time to record information is as soon as it becomes available. You can also coordinate your record keeping to coincide with, for example, monthly financial transactions that would prompt scheduling updates. If you don't have your book handy at that time, jot the information down to add to your book as soon as possible.

18. Confirm the accuracy of your records with outside sources. Call your insurance agent, for example, to verify premiums and relevant dates of policies.

19. Depend upon your Family Record Organizer, not your memory, for the keeping of all records.

20. Make a commitment to yourself to stay organized, with the help of the Family Record Organizer.

Table of Contents

Section 2

Section 3

Section 4

Section 5

Section 6

Section 7

Section 8

Section 9

Section 10

Section 11

Section 1
Family/Personal Records

Form A101   **Alimony/Support Payments** – Records financial history of alimony payments made or received

Form A102   **Apparel Sizing Chart** – Lists clothing sizes for every family member

Form B101   **Baby-sitting Expenses** – Provides a log for hours and costs of baby-sitting services

Form C101   **Child Care Services** – Lists important information concerning available child care sources

Form C102   **Chronological Highlights Diary** – Highlights memorable events during certain years

Form D101   **Daily Journal** – Records notable daily events

Form D102   **Document Finder** – Helps locate important household documents

Form D103   **Driver's Licenses Record** – Records essential license information

Form F101   **Family Celebrations** – Lists upcoming family gatherings

Form F102   **Family Tree** – Tracks your family ancestry

Form F103   **Favorite Recipes** – Helps prepare your favorite dishes

Form F104   **Former Addresses** – Keeps record of past residences

Form G101   **Gift Thank-You List** – Acknowledges gifts received and returned thank-yous

Form G102   **Grocery List** – Itemizes groceries to purchase

Form H101   **Holiday Mailing List** – Lists holiday gifts mailed

Form H102   **Household Chores** – Divides domestic responsibilities among family members

Form I101   **Identification Cards** – Provides vital information on important identification cards

Form I102   **Inventory of Collectibles** – Lists valuable items owned

Form I103	**Items to be Returned** – Keeps track of items borrowed
Form I104	**Items to Return** – Keeps track of items lent
Form M101	**Marriage Records** – Provides vital marriage information
Form M102	**Memorable Quotes/Sayings** – Displays some unforgettable sayings
Form O101	**Oustanding Bills Record** – Catalogs bills to be paid and payment due dates
Form P101	**Personal Fact Sheet** – Directory of vital personal information and family data
Form P102	**Personal Favorites Fact Sheet** – Compilation of favorite personal items
Form P103	**Personal Information Sheet** – Lists important personal documents
Form P104	**Pet Care Registry** – Logs veterinarian visits and treatment given
Form R101	**Record of Accident Claims** – Records any personal accident claims that have been filed
Form R102	**Residential Services Schedule** – Keeps a record of household services and domestic repairs performed
Form T101	**To Do Today** – Reminds you of errands to complete for the day
Form T102	**Traffic Violations Record** – Charts traffic tickets received and related traffic/license information
Form V101	**Vehicle Insurance Register** – Details information on vehicle insurance carrier
Form V102	**Vehicle Registration Record** – Lists vehicle registration and renewal information
Form V103	**Volunteer Record** – Charts volunteer services performed
Form V104	**Voter Registration Sheet** – Lists voter registration information
Form V105	**Voting Record** – Catalogs voting history

ALIMONY/SUPPORT PAYMENTS

Name: _____

Amount Sent/Received	Date Sent/Received	Amount In Arrears	Next Payment Due
$_____	_____	$_____	_____
$_____	_____	$_____	_____
$_____	_____	$_____	_____
$_____	_____	$_____	_____
$_____	_____	$_____	_____
$_____	_____	$_____	_____
$_____	_____	$_____	_____
$_____	_____	$_____	_____
$_____	_____	$_____	_____
$_____	_____	$_____	_____
$_____	_____	$_____	_____
$_____	_____	$_____	_____
$_____	_____	$_____	_____
$_____	_____	$_____	_____
$_____	_____	$_____	_____
$_____	_____	$_____	_____
$_____	_____	$_____	_____
$_____	_____	$_____	_____
$_____	_____	$_____	_____
$_____	_____	$_____	_____
$_____ **Total**		**$_____** **Total**	

FORM A101

APPAREL SIZING CHART

Name:_____ Date:_____ Measurements:_____

    Blouse_____ Shoes _____ Hat_____

    Dress_____ Shirt _____ Suit _____

    Belt _____ Skirt _____ Pants _____

    Slip _____ Vest_____ Coat_____

    Jacket _____ Gloves _____ Other _____

Name:_____ Date:_____ Measurements:_____

    Blouse_____ Shoes _____ Hat_____

    Dress_____ Shirt _____ Suit _____

    Belt _____ Skirt _____ Pants _____

    Slip _____ Vest_____ Coat_____

    Jacket _____ Gloves _____ Other _____

Name:_____ Date:_____ Measurements:_____

    Blouse_____ Shoes _____ Hat_____

    Dress_____ Shirt _____ Suit _____

    Belt _____ Skirt _____ Pants _____

    Slip _____ Vest_____ Coat_____

    Jacket _____ Gloves _____ Other _____

Name:_____ Date:_____ Measurements:_____

    Blouse_____ Shoes _____ Hat_____

    Dress_____ Shirt _____ Suit _____

    Belt _____ Skirt _____ Pants _____

    Slip _____ Vest_____ Coat_____

    Jacket _____ Gloves _____ Other _____

BABY-SITTING EXPENSES

Name: _____

Name of Service	Date	Time Spent	Hours	Rate of Pay	Amount Paid
_____	_____	_____	_____	$ _____	$ _____
_____	_____	_____	_____	$ _____	$ _____
_____	_____	_____	_____	$ _____	$ _____
_____	_____	_____	_____	$ _____	$ _____
_____	_____	_____	_____	$ _____	$ _____
_____	_____	_____	_____	$ _____	$ _____
_____	_____	_____	_____	$ _____	$ _____
_____	_____	_____	_____	$ _____	$ _____
_____	_____	_____	_____	$ _____	$ _____
_____	_____	_____	_____	$ _____	$ _____
_____	_____	_____	_____	$ _____	$ _____
_____	_____	_____	_____	$ _____	$ _____
_____	_____	_____	_____	$ _____	$ _____
_____	_____	_____	_____	$ _____	$ _____
_____	_____	_____	_____	$ _____	$ _____
_____	_____	_____	_____	$ _____	$ _____
_____	_____	_____	_____	$ _____	$ _____
_____	_____	_____	_____	$ _____	$ _____
_____	_____	_____	_____	$ _____	$ _____
_____	_____	_____	_____	$ _____	$ _____
_____	_____	_____	_____	$ _____	$ _____
_____	_____	_____	_____	$ _____	$ _____

Total Hours: _____   Total Paid: $ _____

FORM B101

CHILD CARE SERVICES

Caregiver's Name: _____ Rate:_____

Address:_____ Phone: _____

Days/Hours Available: _____Age: _____

References: _____

Additional Information: _____

_____

Caregiver's Name: _____ Rate:_____

Address:_____ Phone: _____

Days/Hours Available: _____Age: _____

References: _____

Additional Information: _____

_____

Caregiver's Name: _____ Rate:_____

Address:_____ Phone: _____

Days/Hours Available: _____Age: _____

References: _____

Additional Information: _____

_____

Caregiver's Name: _____ Rate:_____

Address:_____ Phone: _____

Days/Hours Available: _____Age: _____

References: _____

Additional Information: _____

_____

CHRONOLOGICAL HIGHLIGHTS DIARY

Name: _____

Infancy/Preschool Years: _____

_____

_____

Elementary School Years: _____

_____

_____

High School Years: _____

_____

_____

_____

College Years:_____

_____

_____

_____

Adult Years: _____

_____

_____

_____

Retirement Years:_____

_____

_____

_____

DAILY JOURNAL

Name: _____

Date: _____ Place: _____

Things I did today: _____

_____

_____

Places I went: _____

_____

_____

Sights I saw: _____

_____

_____

Special moments: _____

_____

_____

Special thoughts: _____

_____

_____

_____

_____

_____

_____

_____

_____

_____

_____

DOCUMENT FINDER

Name:_____ Date: _____

Insurance Documents: _____

Birth Certificates:_____

Instructions in Case of Death: _____

Deeds/Proofs of Ownership: _____

Marriage Certificates: _____

Social Security Cards: _____

Military Records: _____

Divorce Decrees: _____

Mortgage Documents: _____

Bank Passbooks: _____

Passports: _____

Tax Returns: _____

Wills and Trusts: _____

Prenuptial Agreements: _____

Business Papers: _____

Death Certificates: _____

Warranties: _____

Stock Certificates: _____

Other Investment Certificates: _____

Letters of Final Request:_____

Organ Donor Authorizations: _____

Citizenship Papers: _____

Safe Deposit Keys:_____

Financial Records: _____

     FORM D102

DRIVER'S LICENSES RECORD

Name: _____

License #:_____ Issuing State: _____

Date Issued:_____ Expiration Date: _____

Class: _____ Class Vehicle Limitations: _____

Restrictions: _____

Location of License: _____

Cost of Reissuing License: _____

Driver's License Office Location: _____

_____ Phone:_____

Additional Information:_____

_____

_____

Name: _____

License #:_____ Issuing State: _____

Date Issued:_____ Expiration Date: _____

Class: _____ Class Vehicle Limitations: _____

Restrictions: _____

Location of License: _____

Cost of Reissuing License: _____

Driver's License Office Location: _____

_____ Phone:_____

Additional Information:_____

_____

_____

FAMILY CELEBRATIONS

Date   Occasion   Time   Location

_____   _____   _____   _____

_____   _____   _____   _____

_____   _____   _____   _____

_____   _____   _____   _____

_____   _____   _____   _____

_____   _____   _____   _____

_____   _____   _____   _____

_____   _____   _____   _____

_____   _____   _____   _____

_____   _____   _____   _____

_____   _____   _____   _____

_____   _____   _____   _____

_____   _____   _____   _____

_____   _____   _____   _____

_____   _____   _____   _____

_____   _____   _____   _____

_____   _____   _____   _____

_____   _____   _____   _____

_____   _____   _____   _____

_____   _____   _____   _____

_____   _____   _____   _____

_____   _____   _____   _____

_____   _____   _____   _____

FAMILY TREE

You:_____

Father: _____   Mother: _____

Father's   **Mother's**

Father: _____   Father: _____

Mother: _____   Mother: _____

Father's Paternal   **Mother's Paternal**

Grandfather:_____   Grandfather:_____

Grandmother:_____   Grandmother:_____

Father's Maternal   **Mother's Maternal**

Grandfather:_____   Grandfather:_____

Grandmother:_____   Grandmother:_____

Paternal Side: Father's Siblings: _____

_____

Your Paternal Cousins: _____

_____

Your Grandfather's Siblings: _____

_____

Your Grandmother's Siblings:_____

_____

Maternal Side: Mother's Siblings: _____

_____

Your Maternal Cousins: _____

_____

Your Grandfather's Siblings: _____

_____

Your Grandmother's Siblings:_____

_____

FAVORITE RECIPES

For the Preparation of (Dish): _____

Ingredients   Quantity

_____   _____

_____   _____

_____   _____

_____   _____

_____   _____

_____   _____

_____   _____

_____   _____

_____   _____

_____   _____

Directions: _____

_____

_____

_____

_____

_____

_____

_____

Suggested Accompaniments: _____

_____

_____

Occasions when Served: _____

_____

FORM F103

FORMER ADDRESSES

Name: _____

Dates of Residency: _____ to _____

Address: _____

Leased: _____ Owned: _____ Rented: _____

Name of Landlord:_____ Phone: _____

Address: _____

Dates of Residency: _____ to _____

Address: _____

Leased: _____ Owned: _____ Rented: _____

Name of Landlord:_____ Phone: _____

Address: _____

Dates of Residency: _____ to _____

Address: _____

Leased: _____ Owned: _____ Rented: _____

Name of Landlord:_____ Phone: _____

Address: _____

Dates of Residency: _____ to _____

Address: _____

Leased: _____ Owned: _____ Rented: _____

Name of Landlord:_____ Phone: _____

Address: _____

GIFT THANK-YOU LIST

Received From	Gift	Date Gift Received	Date Thank-You Mailed

FORM G101

GROCERY LIST

Date: _____

Item	Price	Coupon (✓)	Checklist (✓)
1. _____	$ _____	_____	_____
2. _____	$ _____	_____	_____
3. _____	$ _____	_____	_____
4. _____	$ _____	_____	_____
5. _____	$ _____	_____	_____
6. _____	$ _____	_____	_____
7. _____	$ _____	_____	_____
8. _____	$ _____	_____	_____
9. _____	$ _____	_____	_____
10. _____	$ _____	_____	_____
11. _____	$ _____	_____	_____
12. _____	$ _____	_____	_____
13. _____	$ _____	_____	_____
14. _____	$ _____	_____	_____
15. _____	$ _____	_____	_____
16. _____	$ _____	_____	_____
17. _____	$ _____	_____	_____
18. _____	$ _____	_____	_____
19. _____	$ _____	_____	_____
20. _____	$ _____	_____	_____
21. _____	$ _____	_____	_____
22. _____	$ _____	_____	_____
23. _____	$ _____	_____	_____
24. _____	$ _____	_____	_____

HOLIDAY MAILING LIST

Name:_____ Year:_____

Gift/Card Recipient	Address	Date Sent
_____	_____	_____
_____	_____	_____
_____	_____	_____
_____	_____	_____
_____	_____	_____
_____	_____	_____
_____	_____	_____
_____	_____	_____
_____	_____	_____
_____	_____	_____
_____	_____	_____
_____	_____	_____
_____	_____	_____
_____	_____	_____
_____	_____	_____
_____	_____	_____
_____	_____	_____
_____	_____	_____
_____	_____	_____
_____	_____	_____
_____	_____	_____
_____	_____	_____
_____	_____	_____
_____	_____	_____

FORM H101

HOUSEHOLD CHORES

Family Member	Duty	Date Assigned	Date Finished

IDENTIFICATION CARDS

Name: _____

Type of Card: _____

Card ID #: _____ Date Issued: _____

Classification: _____ Expiration Date: _____

Conditions/Restrictions: _____

Issuing Authority: _____

Location of Card: _____

Other Information: _____

Type of Card: _____

Card ID #: _____ Date Issued: _____

Classification: _____ Expiration Date: _____

Conditions/Restrictions: _____

Issuing Authority: _____

Location of Card: _____

Other Information: _____

Type of Card: _____

Card ID #: _____ Date Issued: _____

Classification: _____ Expiration Date: _____

Conditions/Restrictions: _____

Issuing Authority: _____

Location of Card: _____

Other Information: _____

INVENTORY OF COLLECTIBLES

Name: _____

Item	Purchase Date	Purchase Price	Estimated Value
_____	_____	$ _____	$ _____
_____	_____	$ _____	$ _____
_____	_____	$ _____	$ _____
_____	_____	$ _____	$ _____
_____	_____	$ _____	$ _____
_____	_____	$ _____	$ _____
_____	_____	$ _____	$ _____
_____	_____	$ _____	$ _____
_____	_____	$ _____	$ _____
_____	_____	$ _____	$ _____
_____	_____	$ _____	$ _____
_____	_____	$ _____	$ _____
_____	_____	$ _____	$ _____
_____	_____	$ _____	$ _____
_____	_____	$ _____	$ _____
_____	_____	$ _____	$ _____
_____	_____	$ _____	$ _____
_____	_____	$ _____	$ _____
_____	_____	$ _____	$ _____
_____	_____	$ _____	$ _____
_____	_____	$ _____	$ _____
Total:		$ _____	$ _____

ITEMS TO BE RETURNED

Item Lent	Borrower	Date Lent	Date Returned	Returned Condition

FORM I103

ITEMS TO RETURN

Item Borrowed	Lender	Date Borrowed	Date Returned	Returned Condition
_____	_____	_____	_____	_____
_____	_____	_____	_____	_____
_____	_____	_____	_____	_____
_____	_____	_____	_____	_____
_____	_____	_____	_____	_____
_____	_____	_____	_____	_____
_____	_____	_____	_____	_____
_____	_____	_____	_____	_____
_____	_____	_____	_____	_____
_____	_____	_____	_____	_____
_____	_____	_____	_____	_____
_____	_____	_____	_____	_____
_____	_____	_____	_____	_____
_____	_____	_____	_____	_____
_____	_____	_____	_____	_____
_____	_____	_____	_____	_____
_____	_____	_____	_____	_____
_____	_____	_____	_____	_____
_____	_____	_____	_____	_____
_____	_____	_____	_____	_____
_____	_____	_____	_____	_____

MARRIAGE RECORDS

Husband's Full Name: _____

Wife's Full Name: _____

Marriage Date: _____ Officiated by: _____

Marriage Location: _____

     City: _____ County: _____ State: _____

Location of Marriage License or Certificate:_____

_____

Additional Information:_____

_____

_____

_____

If Re-Married:

Husband's Full Name: _____

Wife's Full Name: _____

Marriage Date: _____ Officiated by: _____

Marriage Location: _____

     City: _____ County: _____ State: _____

Location of Marriage License or Certificate:_____

_____

Additional Information:_____

_____

_____

_____

MEMORABLE QUOTES/SAYINGS

Quote: _____

_____

_____

Originator: _____Date: _____

Quote: _____

_____

_____

Originator: _____Date: _____

Quote: _____

_____

_____

Originator: _____Date: _____

Quote: _____

_____

_____

Originator: _____Date: _____

Quote: _____

_____

_____

Originator: _____Date: _____

OUTSTANDING BILLS RECORD

Name:_____ Date: _____

Pay To	Date Due	Amount Due	Date Paid	Amount Paid
_____	_____	$_____	_____	$_____
_____	_____	$_____	_____	$_____
_____	_____	$_____	_____	$_____
_____	_____	$_____	_____	$_____
_____	_____	$_____	_____	$_____
_____	_____	$_____	_____	$_____
_____	_____	$_____	_____	$_____
_____	_____	$_____	_____	$_____
_____	_____	$_____	_____	$_____
_____	_____	$_____	_____	$_____
_____	_____	$_____	_____	$_____
_____	_____	$_____	_____	$_____
_____	_____	$_____	_____	$_____
_____	_____	$_____	_____	$_____
_____	_____	$_____	_____	$_____
_____	_____	$_____	_____	$_____
_____	_____	$_____	_____	$_____
_____	_____	$_____	_____	$_____
_____	_____	$_____	_____	$_____
_____	_____	$_____	_____	$_____
_____	_____	$_____	_____	$_____
_____	_____	$_____	_____	$_____
_____	_____	$_____	_____	$_____

FORM O101

PERSONAL FACT SHEET

Name:_____ Birthdate: _____

Birthplace/City: _____ County:_____ State:_____

Social Security #: _____ Blood Type: _____

Driver's License #:_____ State Issued: _____

Location of Birth Certificate: _____

Other Identification: _____ Number: _____

Important Significant Events:

Event   Date

_____   _____

_____   _____

_____   _____

_____   _____

Location of Important Documents:

Name of Document   Location of Document

_____   _____

_____   _____

_____   _____

Marriage Date:_____ Name of Spouse: _____

City:_____ County:_____ State: _____

Birthdate of Spouse:_____ Birthplace:_____

Names of Children   Birthdates   Birthplaces of Children

_____   _____   _____

_____   _____   _____

_____   _____   _____

Other Information: _____

_____

PERSONAL FAVORITES FACT SHEET

Name:_____ Date: _____

Food: _____

City:_____

Color:_____

Book: _____

Author: _____

Sport/Game: _____

Singer/Performer:_____

Concert:_____

Artist: _____

Vacation Spot: _____

Restaurant: _____

Beverage: _____

Movie/Play:_____

Actress: _____

Actor:_____

Comedian: _____

Perfume/Cologne: _____

Politician: _____

Hero: _____

Hobby: _____

Breed of Animal: _____

Others:_____

_____

_____

PERSONAL INFORMATION SHEET

Date: _____

Full Legal Name: _____

Also Known As: _____

Date of Birth: _____Place of Birth: _____

Country of Citizenship: _____

If Naturalized, Date of Naturalization: _____

Place of Naturalization: _____

If Resident Alien, Alien Registration #: _____

Social Security #: _____

Address: _____

Home Phone: _____ Work Phone: _____

Employer: _____

Employer Address: _____

Bank Account #: _____ Bank Name: _____

Driver's License #: _____ State: _____ Expires: _____

Health Insurance: _____ Policy #: _____

Medical Insurance: _____ Policy #: _____

Dental Insurance: _____ Policy #: _____

Allergies: _____

Medical Problems: _____

Blood Type: _____ Organ Donor: (Yes) _____ (No) _____

If Veteran, Branch of Service, Unit: _____

Rank or Rate at Discharge: _____ Date Discharged: _____

In Case of an Emergency, Please Contact

Name:_____Phone: _____

Relation: _____

PET CARE REGISTRY

Date of Visit:_____

Pet's Name: _____ Age: _____

Breed: _____ Color(s): _____

Name of Veterinarian:_____

Name of Clinic/Animal Hospital: _____

Location: _____ Phone: _____

Reason: _____

Diagnosis: _____

Treatment: _____

Cost: $ _____

Next Appointment Scheduled: _____ Time: _____

Reason: _____

_____

Date of Visit:_____

Pet's Name: _____ Age: _____

Breed: _____ Color(s): _____

Name of Veterinarian:_____

Name of Clinic/Animal Hospital: _____

Location: _____ Phone: _____

Reason: _____

Diagnosis: _____

Treatment: _____

Cost: $ _____

Next Appointment Scheduled: _____ Time: _____

Reason: _____

_____

FORM P104

RECORD OF ACCIDENT CLAIMS

Name: _____

Claim Filed Against: _____ Filing Date:_____

Date of Accident:_____ Location: _____

Description of Claim: _____

_____

_____

Court: _____ Case #: _____ Phone: _____

Attorney: _____ Phone: _____

Other Information: _____

_____

_____

_____

Name: _____

Claim Filed Against: _____ Filing Date:_____

Date of Accident:_____ Location: _____

Description of Claim: _____

_____

_____

Court: _____ Case #: _____ Phone: _____

Attorney: _____ Phone: _____

Other Information: _____

_____

_____

_____

RESIDENTIAL SERVICES SCHEDULE

Name: _____

Name of Company: _____ Date: _____
Service Required: _____
Amount Charged: $ _____ Amount Paid: $ _____ Balance: $_____

Name of Company: _____ Date: _____
Service Required: _____
Amount Charged: $ _____ Amount Paid: $ _____ Balance: $_____

Name of Company: _____ Date: _____
Service Required: _____
Amount Charged: $ _____ Amount Paid: $ _____ Balance: $_____

Name of Company: _____ Date: _____
Service Required: _____
Amount Charged: $ _____ Amount Paid: $ _____ Balance: $_____

Name of Company: _____ Date: _____
Service Required: _____
Amount Charged: $ _____ Amount Paid: $ _____ Balance: $_____

Name of Company: _____ Date: _____
Service Required: _____
Amount Charged: $ _____ Amount Paid: $ _____ Balance: $_____

FORM R102

TO DO TODAY

Name:_____ Day:_____ Date: _____

Appointments   Time

_____   _____

_____   _____

_____   _____

_____   _____

Tasks to be Completed   (✓) if Done

_____   _____

_____   _____

_____   _____

_____   _____

Calls to Make   Phone

_____   _____

_____   _____

_____   _____

_____   _____

Errands to Run

_____   _____

_____   _____

_____   _____

Other Information: _____

_____

TRAFFIC VIOLATIONS RECORD

Name:_____ Date: _____

Tickets Received

Ticket #: _____ Description: _____

Date: _____ Cost: $ _____ Points: _____

Ticket #: _____ Description: _____

Date: _____ Cost: $ _____ Points: _____

Ticket #: _____ Description: _____

Date: _____ Cost: $ _____ Points: _____

Ticket #: _____ Description: _____

Date: _____ Cost: $ _____ Points: _____

Total Points: _____

Defensive Driving Courses Taken:
Reason   Date

_____   _____

_____   _____

_____   _____

License Suspension/Revocation:
Reason   Date Began   Date Ended

_____   _____   _____

_____   _____   _____

_____   _____   _____

Additional Traffic-Related Charges: _____

_____

Additional Information:_____

_____

FORM T102

VEHICLE INSURANCE REGISTER

Vehicle Information

Title Holder: _____ Date: _____

License Plate #: _____ ID #: _____ State: _____

Make of Vehicle: _____ Model: _____ Year:_____

Registration #: _____ Expiration Date: _____

Insurance Information

Insurance Company:_____

Policy #: _____ Deductible Amount: $ _____

Liability Amount: _____

Other Coverages:_____

Annual Premium:_____ Due Date(s): _____

Agent's Name: _____

Address of Agent: _____

Agent's Phone:_____ Service/Claims Phone: _____

Policy Location: _____

Miscellaneous Details: _____

_____

_____

_____

_____

_____

_____

_____

_____

VEHICLE REGISTRATION RECORD

Vehicle Owner:_____

Vehicle Description: _____

License Plate #:_____ State: _____

Registration Year: _____

Registration Renewal Fee: _____ Date Due: _____

Vehicle Owner:_____

Vehicle Description: _____

License Plate # _____ State: _____

Registration Year: _____

Registration Renewal Fee: _____ Date Due: _____

Vehicle Owner:_____

Vehicle Description: _____

License Plate #:_____ State: _____

Registration Year: _____

Registration Renewal Fee: _____ Date Due: _____

Vehicle Owner:_____

Vehicle Description: _____

License Plate #:_____ State: _____

Registration Year: _____

Registration Renewal Fee: _____ Date Due: _____

 FORM V102

VOLUNTEER RECORD

Name: _____

Place Volunteered:_____

Location: _____ Phone: _____

Duties: _____

_____

Supervisor: _____

Dates Worked   Hours Worked

_____   _____

_____   _____

_____   _____

_____   _____

_____   _____

_____   _____

_____   _____

_____   _____

_____   _____

Total Volunteer Hours:_____

Comments: _____

_____

_____

_____

_____

_____

VOTER REGISTRATION SHEET

Name:_____ Date: _____

Voter Residence Address: _____

_____

Registration Date: _____

Registration Card #: _____

Party Registered as: _____

Voting Precinct:_____ Voting Location: _____

Additional Information:_____

Name:_____ Date: _____

Voter Residence Address: _____

_____

Registration Date: _____

Registration Card #: _____

Party Registered as: _____

Voting Precinct:_____ Voting Location: _____

Additional Information:_____

Name:_____ Date: _____

Voter Residence Address: _____

_____

Registration Date: _____

Registration Card #: _____

Party Registered as: _____

Voting Precinct:_____ Voting Location: _____

Additional Information:_____

FORM V104

VOTING RECORD

Name: _____

Election Date: _____ Voting Location: _____

Public Office Position: _____

Candidates: _____ _____

_____ _____

_____ _____

Candidate Voted For: _____

Party Voted For: _____

Election Results: _____

Election Date: _____ Voting Location: _____

Public Office Position: _____

Candidates: _____ _____

_____ _____

_____ _____

Candidate Voted For: _____

Party Voted For: _____

Election Results: _____

Election Date: _____ Voting Location: _____

Public Office Position: _____

Candidates: _____ _____

_____ _____

_____ _____

Candidate Voted For: _____

Party Voted For: _____

Election Results: _____

Section 2
Business Forms

Form A201   **Advertising Budget** – Charts money spent for various advertising methods

Form A202   **Advertising Directory** – Records names, contracts and billing information for current or potential advertising media

Form A203   **Advertising Record** – Lists customer responses from advertisements

Form A204   **Applications Pending** – Lists job, credit or school applications and responses

Form A205   **Appointments** – Keeps track of weekly scheduled appointments

Form B201   **Business Holdings Register** – Records business interests held

Form C201   **Contacts Made** – Reference guide for business contacts made

Form D201   **Daily Auto Mileage Ledger** – Itemizes business expenses incurred

Form E201   **Employee Benefit Package** – Details benefit packages

Form H201   **Home Office Product Order Form** – Lists office products to order

Form H202   **Hourly Work Schedule** – Keeps daily record of hours worked and wages earned

Form J201   **Job Estimates** – Provides listing of contractors' job estimates given

Form J202   **Job History Record** – Provides record of previous employment held

Form L201   **Limited Partnership Log** – Records ownership information in a limited partnership

Form L202	**Long Distance Phone Call Record** – Keeps listing of long distance phone calls made
Form M201	**Meeting Agenda** – Schedule of business meeting activities
Form M202	**Meeting Schedule** – Listing of planned business meetings
Form O201	**Occupational License Listing** – Provides pertinent information on occupational licenses issued
Form P201	**Patents Received** – Provides data on patents issued
Form R201	**Record of Attendance** – Tracks dates of attendance
Form R202	**Rental Real Estate** – Lists property payment information
Form S201	**Sales Prospects** – Records correspondence with prospective clients
Form S202	**Sales Record** – Itemizes sales accounts made
Form S203	**Schedule of Business Trips** – Summarizes appointments held on business trips
Form S204	**Software Inventory** – Catalogs computer software owned
Form U201	**Utilities Cost Inventory** – Keeps inventory of monthly utility costs

ADVERTISING BUDGET/19____

Company Name: _____

Month	Radio	Television	Newspaper	Other	Monthly Cost
January:	_____	_____	_____	_____	_____
February:	_____	_____	_____	_____	_____
March:	_____	_____	_____	_____	_____
April:	_____	_____	_____	_____	_____
May:	_____	_____	_____	_____	_____
June:	_____	_____	_____	_____	_____
July:	_____	_____	_____	_____	_____
August:	_____	_____	_____	_____	_____
September:	_____	_____	_____	_____	_____
October:	_____	_____	_____	_____	_____
November:	_____	_____	_____	_____	_____
December:	_____	_____	_____	_____	_____

Total Yearly Advertising Cost: $ _____

FORM A201

ADVERTISING DIRECTORY

Medium: _____

Station/Publication Name: _____

Contact Person: _____

Advertising Contract: _____ to _____

Rate: _____

Billing Address: _____

Phone: _____

Medium: _____

Station/Publication Name: _____

Contact Person: _____

Advertising Contract: _____ to _____

Rate: _____

Billing Address: _____

Phone: _____

Medium: _____

Station/Publication Name: _____

Contact Person: _____

Advertising Contract: _____ to _____

Rate: _____

Billing Address: _____

Phone: _____

ADVERTISING RECORD

Item Advertised	Date(s) Ad Aired/ Published	Advertising Medium	Number of Respondents	Sales Results
_____	_____	_____	_____	_____
_____	_____	_____	_____	_____
_____	_____	_____	_____	_____
_____	_____	_____	_____	_____
_____	_____	_____	_____	_____
_____	_____	_____	_____	_____
_____	_____	_____	_____	_____
_____	_____	_____	_____	_____
_____	_____	_____	_____	_____
_____	_____	_____	_____	_____
_____	_____	_____	_____	_____
_____	_____	_____	_____	_____
_____	_____	_____	_____	_____
_____	_____	_____	_____	_____
_____	_____	_____	_____	_____
_____	_____	_____	_____	_____
_____	_____	_____	_____	_____
_____	_____	_____	_____	_____
_____	_____	_____	_____	_____
_____	_____	_____	_____	_____
_____	_____	_____	_____	_____
_____	_____	_____	_____	_____
_____	_____	_____	_____	_____

FORM A203

APPLICATIONS PENDING

Name: _____

Applied to: _____ Date: _____

Address: _____

Contact Name: _____ Phone: _____

Date of Follow-Up Contact: _____

Response: _____

_____

Applied to: _____ Date: _____

Address: _____

Contact Name: _____ Phone: _____

Date of Follow-Up Contact: _____

Response: _____

_____

Applied to: _____ Date: _____

Address: _____

Contact Name: _____ Phone: _____

Date of Follow-Up Contact: _____

Response: _____

_____

APPOINTMENTS

Name:_____ Week of: _____

	Appointment with	Concerning	Phone	Time
Sunday:	_____	_____	_____	_____
	_____	_____	_____	_____
Monday:	_____	_____	_____	_____
	_____	_____	_____	_____
Tuesday:	_____	_____	_____	_____
	_____	_____	_____	_____
Wednesday:	_____	_____	_____	_____
	_____	_____	_____	_____
Thursday:	_____	_____	_____	_____
	_____	_____	_____	_____
Friday:	_____	_____	_____	_____
	_____	_____	_____	_____
Saturday:	_____	_____	_____	_____
	_____	_____	_____	_____

Notes: _____

_____

FORM A205

BUSINESS HOLDINGS REGISTER

Name of Owner:_____ Date: _____

Name of Business:_____

Location: _____

Ownership Interest %: _____

Amount Paid: $ _____ Present Value: $ _____

Evidence of Ownership:_____

_____

Name of Owner:_____ Date: _____

Name of Business:_____

Location: _____

Ownership Interest %: _____

Amount Paid: $ _____ Present Value: $ _____

Evidence of Ownership:_____

_____

Name of Owner:_____ Date: _____

Name of Business:_____

Location: _____

Ownership Interest %: _____

Amount Paid: $ _____ Present Value: $ _____

Evidence of Ownership:_____

_____

CONTACTS MADE

Name of Business Contact: _____

Company: _____

Person's Title: _____ Phone: _____

Met at: _____ Date: _____

Issues Discussed: _____

Additional Information: _____

_____

Name of Business Contact: _____

Company: _____

Person's Title: _____ Phone: _____

Met at: _____ Date: _____

Issues Discussed: _____

Additional Information: _____

_____

Name of Business Contact: _____

Company: _____

Person's Title: _____ Phone: _____

Met at: _____ Date: _____

Issues Discussed: _____

Additional Information: _____

_____

FORM C201

DAILY AUTO MILEAGE LEDGER

Name:_____ Year:_____

Date	Destination	Purpose	Miles	Other Costs
_____	_____	_____	_____	$_____
_____	_____	_____	_____	$_____
_____	_____	_____	_____	$_____
_____	_____	_____	_____	$_____
_____	_____	_____	_____	$_____
_____	_____	_____	_____	$_____
_____	_____	_____	_____	$_____
_____	_____	_____	_____	$_____
_____	_____	_____	_____	$_____
_____	_____	_____	_____	$_____
_____	_____	_____	_____	$_____
_____	_____	_____	_____	$_____
_____	_____	_____	_____	$_____
_____	_____	_____	_____	$_____
_____	_____	_____	_____	$_____
_____	_____	_____	_____	$_____
_____	_____	_____	_____	$_____
_____	_____	_____	_____	$_____
_____	_____	_____	_____	$_____
_____	_____	_____	_____	$_____
_____	_____	_____	_____	$_____
_____	_____	_____	_____	$_____
_____	_____	_____	_____	$_____

Total: $ _____ $_____

EMPLOYEE BENEFIT PACKAGE

Name of Insured: _____ Insurance #:_____

Name of Employer:_____

Insurance Provider:_____

Company Contact: _____ Phone: _____

Benefit Plan Location:_____

Other Plan Information:_____

_____

Benefit Plan Effective Date: _____

List of Benefits Available:

Stock Options	$ _____
Restricted Stock	$ _____
Group Life Insurance	$ _____
Deferred Compensation	$ _____
Vested Employer's Contribution	$ _____
Savings Plan Contribution	$ _____
Vested Employee's Contribution	$ _____
Profit Sharing Plan Contribution	$ _____
Pension Plan Contribution	$ _____
Post-Death Salary Compensation	$ _____
Other	
_____	$ _____
_____	$ _____
_____	$ _____

FORM E201

HOME OFFICE PRODUCT ORDER FORM

Name: _____

Product	Date Orderd	Vendor	Quantity	Price
_____	_____	_____	_____	$ _____
_____	_____	_____	_____	$ _____
_____	_____	_____	_____	$ _____
_____	_____	_____	_____	$ _____
_____	_____	_____	_____	$ _____
_____	_____	_____	_____	$ _____
_____	_____	_____	_____	$ _____
_____	_____	_____	_____	$ _____
_____	_____	_____	_____	$ _____
_____	_____	_____	_____	$ _____
_____	_____	_____	_____	$ _____
_____	_____	_____	_____	$ _____
_____	_____	_____	_____	$ _____
_____	_____	_____	_____	$ _____
_____	_____	_____	_____	$ _____
_____	_____	_____	_____	$ _____
_____	_____	_____	_____	$ _____
_____	_____	_____	_____	$ _____
_____	_____	_____	_____	$ _____
_____	_____	_____	_____	$ _____
_____	_____	_____	_____	$ _____
_____	_____	_____	_____	$ _____

Total Price: $ _____

HOURLY WORK SCHEDULE

Name: _____

Employer: _____

Location: _____

Salary/Hr.: _____

Hours Worked:

Week of:	Sun.	Mon.	Tue.	Wed.	Thur.	Fri.	Sat.	Total Hours	Total Pay	Date Paid
_____	____	____	____	____	____	____	____	____	____	____
_____	____	____	____	____	____	____	____	____	____	____
_____	____	____	____	____	____	____	____	____	____	____
_____	____	____	____	____	____	____	____	____	____	____
_____	____	____	____	____	____	____	____	____	____	____
_____	____	____	____	____	____	____	____	____	____	____
_____	____	____	____	____	____	____	____	____	____	____
_____	____	____	____	____	____	____	____	____	____	____
_____	____	____	____	____	____	____	____	____	____	____
_____	____	____	____	____	____	____	____	____	____	____
_____	____	____	____	____	____	____	____	____	____	____
_____	____	____	____	____	____	____	____	____	____	____
_____	____	____	____	____	____	____	____	____	____	____
_____	____	____	____	____	____	____	____	____	____	____
_____	____	____	____	____	____	____	____	____	____	____
_____	____	____	____	____	____	____	____	____	____	____
_____	____	____	____	____	____	____	____	____	____	____
_____	____	____	____	____	____	____	____	____	____	____

FORM H202

JOB ESTIMATES

Project: _____

_____

Contractor: _____

Address: _____

Phone: _____ Bid: _____

Start Date: _____ Project Completion Date: _____

Additional Information: _____

_____

Contractor: _____

Address: _____

Phone: _____ Bid: _____

Start Date: _____ Project Completion Date: _____

Additional Information: _____

_____

Contractor: _____

Address: _____

Phone: _____ Bid: _____

Start Date: _____ Project Completion Date: _____

Additional Information: _____

_____

JOB HISTORY RECORD

Name: _____

Employer: _____

Address: _____

Type of Business/Organization: _____

Title/Position: _____ Hrs./Wk.: _____

Dates Employed: from _____ to _____

Starting Salary: $ _____ Ending Salary: $ _____

Job Responsibilities: _____

_____

Name of Supervisor: _____

Reason for Leaving: _____

Comments: _____

_____

Employer: _____

Address: _____

Type of Business/Organization: _____

Title/Position: _____ Hrs./Wk.: _____

Dates Employed: from _____ to _____

Starting Salary: $ _____ Ending Salary: $ _____

Job Responsibilities: _____

_____

Name of Supervisor: _____

Reason for Leaving: _____

Comments: _____

_____

FORM J202

LIMITED PARTNERSHIP LOG

Name of Partnership	Date Partnership Formed	Percent of Ownership Interest	General or Limited Partner	Amount of Investment
_____	_____	_____	_____	_____
_____	_____	_____	_____	_____
_____	_____	_____	_____	_____
_____	_____	_____	_____	_____
_____	_____	_____	_____	_____
_____	_____	_____	_____	_____
_____	_____	_____	_____	_____
_____	_____	_____	_____	_____
_____	_____	_____	_____	_____
_____	_____	_____	_____	_____
_____	_____	_____	_____	_____
_____	_____	_____	_____	_____
_____	_____	_____	_____	_____
_____	_____	_____	_____	_____
_____	_____	_____	_____	_____
_____	_____	_____	_____	_____
_____	_____	_____	_____	_____
_____	_____	_____	_____	_____
_____	_____	_____	_____	_____
_____	_____	_____	_____	_____
_____	_____	_____	_____	_____
_____	_____	_____	_____	_____

LONG DISTANCE PHONE CALL RECORD

Date	Name of Caller	Party Called	Number Called	Time from - to
_____	_____	_____	_____	_____
_____	_____	_____	_____	_____
_____	_____	_____	_____	_____
_____	_____	_____	_____	_____
_____	_____	_____	_____	_____
_____	_____	_____	_____	_____
_____	_____	_____	_____	_____
_____	_____	_____	_____	_____
_____	_____	_____	_____	_____
_____	_____	_____	_____	_____
_____	_____	_____	_____	_____
_____	_____	_____	_____	_____
_____	_____	_____	_____	_____
_____	_____	_____	_____	_____
_____	_____	_____	_____	_____
_____	_____	_____	_____	_____
_____	_____	_____	_____	_____
_____	_____	_____	_____	_____
_____	_____	_____	_____	_____
_____	_____	_____	_____	_____
_____	_____	_____	_____	_____
_____	_____	_____	_____	_____
_____	_____	_____	_____	_____

FORM L202

MEETING AGENDA

Organization: _____

Meeting Date: _____ Location: _____

Agenda Issues   Action Taken

_____   _____

_____   _____

_____   _____

_____   _____

_____   _____

_____   _____

_____   _____

_____   _____

Additional Discussion: _____

_____

_____

_____

Persons Attending

_____ _____ _____

_____ _____ _____

_____ _____ _____

_____ _____ _____

_____ _____ _____

_____ _____ _____

_____ _____ _____

MEETING SCHEDULE

Name: _____

Meeting with: _____ Date: _____

Time:_____ Location: _____

Contact Person:_____ Phone: _____

Name: _____

Meeting with: _____ Date: _____

Time:_____ Location: _____

Contact Person:_____ Phone: _____

Name: _____

Meeting with: _____ Date: _____

Time:_____ Location: _____

Contact Person:_____ Phone: _____

Name: _____

Meeting with: _____ Date: _____

Time:_____ Location: _____

Contact Person:_____ Phone: _____

Name: _____

Meeting with: _____ Date: _____

Time:_____ Location: _____

Contact Person:_____ Phone: _____

FORM M202

OCCUPATIONAL LICENSE LISTING

Name: _____

License Title: _____

License #: _____

Purpose: _____

Issued by: _____

Date Issued:_____ Date Expires: _____

License Renewal Fee: _____

Additional Information: _____

License Title: _____

License #: _____

Purpose: _____

Issued by: _____

Date Issued:_____ Date Expires: _____

License Renewal Fee: _____

Additional Information: _____

License Title: _____

License #: _____

Purpose: _____

Issued by: _____

Date Issued:_____ Date Expires: _____

License Renewal Fee: _____

Additional Information: _____

PATENTS RECEIVED

Name: _____

Patent #: _____

Patent Description: _____

_____

Date Applied for: _____ Date Issued: _____

Patent Expiration Date: _____

Other Information: _____

Patent #: _____

Patent Description: _____

_____

Date Applied for: _____ Date Issued: _____

Patent Expiration Date: _____

Other Information: _____

Patent #: _____

Patent Description: _____

_____

Date Applied for: _____ Date Issued: _____

Patent Expiration Date: _____

Other Information: _____

Patent #: _____

Patent Description: _____

_____

Date Applied for: _____ Date Issued: _____

Patent Expiration Date: _____

Other Information: _____

FORM P201

RECORD OF ATTENDANCE

Name: _____ Year: _____

Place of Attendance: _____

	Jan.	Feb.	Mar.	Apr.	May	June	July	Aug.	Sept.	Oct.	Nov.	Dec.
1												
2												
3												
4												
5												
6												
7												
8												
9												
10												
11												
12												
13												
14												
15												
16												
17												
18												
19												
20												
21												
22												
23												
24												
25												
26												
27												
28												
29												
30												
31												

Total: _____ _____ _____ _____ _____ _____ _____ _____ _____ _____ _____ _____

RENTAL REAL ESTATE

Location of Property: _____

Description of Property: _____

_____

Tenants: _____ Phone: _____

Rental Date: from _____ to _____

Terms of Rental Agreement: _____

_____

_____

_____

Rent: _____ Due: _____

Other Information: _____

_____

Location of Property: _____

Description of Property: _____

_____

Tenants: _____ Phone: _____

Rental Date: from _____ to _____

Terms of Rental Agreement: _____

_____

_____

_____

Rent: _____ Due: _____

Other Information: _____

_____

FORM R202

SALES PROSPECTS

Date: _____

Name of Prospect/Business: _____

Address: _____

Contact: _____ Phone: _____ Date of Call: _____

Results: _____

Name of Prospect/Business: _____

Address: _____

Contact: _____ Phone: _____ Date of Call: _____

Results: _____

Name of Prospect/Business: _____

Address: _____

Contact: _____ Phone: _____ Date of Call: _____

Results: _____

Name of Prospect/Business: _____

Address: _____

Contact: _____ Phone: _____ Date of Call: _____

Results: _____

Name of Prospect/Business: _____

Address: _____

Contact: _____ Phone: _____ Date of Call: _____

Results: _____

SALES RECORD

Name: _____

Name of Account	Account #	Date of Sale	Amount of Sale
_____	_____	_____	$ _____
_____	_____	_____	$ _____
_____	_____	_____	$ _____
_____	_____	_____	$ _____
_____	_____	_____	$ _____
_____	_____	_____	$ _____
_____	_____	_____	$ _____
_____	_____	_____	$ _____
_____	_____	_____	$ _____
_____	_____	_____	$ _____
_____	_____	_____	$ _____
_____	_____	_____	$ _____
_____	_____	_____	$ _____
_____	_____	_____	$ _____
_____	_____	_____	$ _____
_____	_____	_____	$ _____
_____	_____	_____	$ _____
_____	_____	_____	$ _____
_____	_____	_____	$ _____
_____	_____	_____	$ _____
_____	_____	_____	$ _____
		Total Sales:	$ _____

FORM S202

SCHEDULE OF BUSINESS TRIPS

Traveler's Name: _____ Date: _____

Destination: _____

Date of Arrival: _____ Time: _____

Date of Return: _____ Time: _____

Appointment with: _____ Position: _____

Company: _____ Phone: _____

Address: _____

Date:_____ from: _____ to: _____

Topic of Meeting:_____

Appointment with: _____ Position: _____

Company: _____ Phone: _____

Address: _____

Date:_____ from: _____ to: _____

Topic of Meeting:_____

Appointment with: _____ Position: _____

Company: _____ Phone: _____

Address: _____

Date:_____ from: _____ to: _____

Topic of Meeting:_____

Appointment with: _____ Position: _____

Company: _____ Phone: _____

Address: _____

Date:_____ from: _____ to: _____

Topic of Meeting:_____

SOFTWARE INVENTORY

ID #	Name/Title	Computer	Location	Version

FORM S204

UTILITIES COST INVENTORY

Name: _____

Utility	Billing Date	Cost This Month	Cost Last Month
_____	_____	$_____	$_____
_____	_____	$_____	$_____
_____	_____	$_____	$_____
_____	_____	$_____	$_____
_____	_____	$_____	$_____
_____	_____	$_____	$_____
_____	_____	$_____	$_____
_____	_____	$_____	$_____
_____	_____	$_____	$_____
_____	_____	$_____	$_____
_____	_____	$_____	$_____
_____	_____	$_____	$_____
_____	_____	$_____	$_____
_____	_____	$_____	$_____
_____	_____	$_____	$_____
_____	_____	$_____	$_____
_____	_____	$_____	$_____
_____	_____	$_____	$_____
_____	_____	$_____	$_____
_____	_____	$_____	$_____
_____	_____	$_____	$_____
_____	_____	$_____	$_____
Total:		$_____	$_____

Section 3
Educational Records

Form C301   **Course Assignments** – Lists school assignments to be completed

Form C302   **Curriculum** – Lists student's school schedule

Form E301   **Educational Courses and Seminars** – Listing of courses taken and seminars attended

Form G301   **Grade School Record** – Educational information from elementary school years

Form H301   **High School Record** – Educational information from high school years

Form M301   **Military Service Record** – Provides information on military-related activities

Form P301   **Personal Report Card** – Keeps record of homework, quiz and exam scores

Form S301   **Scholastic College Record** – Compiles educational information from colleges and universities attended

Form S302   **Special Commendations/Awards** – Celebrates awards and special recognition received

Form S303   **Standardized Test Scores** – Records scores and other information for all standardized tests taken

Form V301   **Vocational/Professional Training** – Lists vocational and other training courses taken

COURSE ASSIGNMENTS

Name of Student: _____ Week of: _____

Course: _____

Assignment: _____

Supplies/Materials Needed: _____

_____

Preparation Methods: _____

_____

Additional Information: _____

_____

Estimated Completion Time: _____

Date Assigned: _____ Due Date: _____ Time Due: _____

Course: _____

Assignment: _____

Supplies/Materials Needed: _____

_____

Preparation Methods: _____

_____

Additional Information: _____

_____

Estimated Completion Time: _____

Date Assigned: _____ Due Date: _____ Time Due: _____

CURRICULUM

Name of Student: _____Date:_____

School: _____

	Class/Instructor	Hours	Room

	Class/Instructor	Hours	Room
Monday:	_____	_____ to _____	_____
	_____	_____ to _____	_____
	_____	_____ to _____	_____
	_____	_____ to _____	_____
Tuesday:	_____	_____ to _____	_____
	_____	_____ to _____	_____
	_____	_____ to _____	_____
	_____	_____ to _____	_____
Wednesday:	_____	_____ to _____	_____
	_____	_____ to _____	_____
	_____	_____ to _____	_____
	_____	_____ to _____	_____
Thursday:	_____	_____ to _____	_____
	_____	_____ to _____	_____
	_____	_____ to _____	_____
	_____	_____ to _____	_____
Friday:	_____	_____ to _____	_____
	_____	_____ to _____	_____
	_____	_____ to _____	_____
	_____	_____ to _____	_____
Saturday:	_____	_____ to _____	_____
	_____	_____ to _____	_____
	_____	_____ to _____	_____
	_____	_____ to _____	_____

FORM C302

EDUCATIONAL COURSES AND SEMINARS

Name of Student: _____

Title/Number of Course:_____

Location: _____

Dates Attended:_____ to _____ Total Hours/Credits: _____

Instructor's Name: _____

Grade Earned: _____ Certificate/Diploma:_____

Other Information: _____

_____

Name of Student: _____

Title/Number of Course:_____

Location: _____

Dates Attended:_____ to _____ Total Hours/Credits: _____

Instructor's Name: _____

Grade Earned: _____ Certificate/Diploma:_____

Other Information: _____

_____

Name of Student: _____

Title/Number of Course:_____

Location: _____

Dates Attended:_____ to _____ Total Hours/Credits: _____

Instructor's Name: _____

Grade Earned: _____ Certificate/Diploma:_____

Other Information: _____

_____

GRADE SCHOOL RECORD

Name of Student: _____

School Attended: _____

Location: _____ Phone: _____

Dates Attended: _____ to _____ Grades Completed: _____

Graduation Date: _____ Grade Point Average: _____

Activities: _____

Honors/Awards: _____

Other Information: _____

School Attended: _____

Location: _____ Phone: _____

Dates Attended: _____ to _____ Grades Completed: _____

Graduation Date: _____ Grade Point Average: _____

Activities: _____

Honors/Awards: _____

Other Information: _____

School Attended: _____

Location: _____ Phone: _____

Dates Attended: _____ to _____ Grades Completed: _____

Graduation Date: _____ Grade Point Average: _____

Activities: _____

Honors/Awards: _____

Other Information: _____

FORM G301

HIGH SCHOOL RECORD

Name of Student: _____

School Attended: _____

Location: _____ Phone: _____

Dates Attended: _____ to _____ Grades Completed: _____

Graduation Date: _____ Overall Grade Point Average: _____

Clubs/Activities: _____

_____

_____

Sports Participated In: _____

_____

Honors/Awards: _____

_____

_____

Advanced Placement (AP) Courses:

Course	Date Taken	AP Test Grade	College Credit
_____	_____to_____	_____	_____
_____	_____to_____	_____	_____
_____	_____to_____	_____	_____
_____	_____to_____	_____	_____

PSAT:

Date Taken: _____ Score Received: _____

SAT:

Date Taken: _____ Score Received: _____

Practical Skills/Experience Acquired: _____

_____

MILITARY SERVICE RECORD

Name: _____

Branch of Service:_____ Service #: _____

Selective Service Registration Date: _____

Date of Valid Department of Defense Form DD-214: _____

Years of Service:_____ Date Completed Service:_____

Type of Discharge:_____

Military Occupation Specialty, Number and Title: _____

_____

Beginning Rate/Rank:_____ Date: _____

Promotions	Date	Additional Responsibilities
_____	_____	_____
_____	_____	_____
_____	_____	_____
_____	_____	_____

Medals, Awards Received:_____

_____

Military Programs Involved In: _____

_____

Special Training/Skills: _____

_____

Official Military Benefits:_____

_____

_____

Other Information: _____

_____

FORM M301

PERSONAL REPORT CARD

Name: _____

Course: _____ Credits: _____ Instructor: _____

Course Taken at: _____ Date: _____ to _____

Grades:

Homework _____ _____ _____ _____ _____ _____ _____ _____

_____ _____ _____ _____ _____ _____ _____ _____

_____ _____ _____ _____ _____ _____ _____ _____

_____ _____ _____ _____ _____ _____ _____ _____

Quizzes _____ _____ _____ _____ _____ _____ _____ _____

Exams _____ _____ _____ _____ _____ _____ _____ _____

Project _____ Points/Grade _____

Project _____ Points/Grade _____

Project _____ Points/Grade _____

Midterm Grade _____ Final Grade _____

Course: _____ Credits: _____ Instructor: _____

Course Taken at: _____ Date: _____ to _____

Grades:

Homework _____ _____ _____ _____ _____ _____ _____ _____

_____ _____ _____ _____ _____ _____ _____ _____

_____ _____ _____ _____ _____ _____ _____ _____

_____ _____ _____ _____ _____ _____ _____ _____

Quizzes _____ _____ _____ _____ _____ _____ _____ _____

Exams _____ _____ _____ _____ _____ _____ _____ _____

Project _____ Points/Grade _____

Project _____ Points/Grade _____

Project _____ Points/Grade _____

Midterm Grade _____ Final Grade _____

SCHOLASTIC COLLEGE RECORD

Name of Student: _____

Name of College/University: _____

School Address: _____ Phone: _____

Dates Attended: _____ to _____ Total Years: _____

Major: _____ Major GPA: _____

Minor: _____ Minor GPA: _____

Cumulative GPA: _____ Total Credits: _____

Degree(s) Earned: _____ Date: _____

_____ Date: _____

Tests:	Date Taken	Score	Percentile		Date Taken	Score	Percentile
CLAST	_____	_____	_____	GRE	_____	_____	_____
LSAT	_____	_____	_____	MCAT	_____	_____	_____

Honors/Awards/Scholarships: _____

_____

_____

Clubs/Activities: _____

_____

_____

Practical Experience/Skills Acquired: _____

_____

_____

Comments/Other Information: _____

_____

_____

_____

FORM S301

SPECIAL COMMENDATIONS/AWARDS

Name of Award Recipient: _____

Award/Honor/Special Recognition Received: _____

_____ Date Received: _____

Accomplishment Honored: _____

_____

Other Relevant Information: _____

_____

_____

Name of Award Recipient: _____

Award/Honor/Special Recognition Received: _____

_____ Date Received: _____

Accomplishment Honored: _____

_____

Other Relevant Information: _____

_____

_____

Name of Award Recipient: _____

Award/Honor/Special Recognition Received: _____

_____ Date Received: _____

Accomplishment Honored: _____

_____

Other Relevant Information: _____

_____

STANDARDIZED TEST SCORES

Name:_____ Age: _____

Test: _____ Score: _____ Percentile: _____

Date Taken:_____ Test Location: _____

Purpose of Test: _____

Retest Score, if Applicable: _____ Retest Date: _____

Deadline to Reapply for Next Testing: _____

Test Cost: _____ Additional Fees: _____

Contact Person:_____ Phone: _____

Name:_____ Age: _____

Test: _____ Score: _____ Percentile: _____

Date Taken:_____ Test Location: _____

Purpose of Test: _____

Retest Score, if Applicable: _____ Retest Date: _____

Deadline to Reapply for Next Testing: _____

Test Cost: _____ Additional Fees: _____

Contact Person:_____ Phone: _____

Name:_____ Age: _____

Test: _____ Score: _____ Percentile: _____

Date Taken:_____ Test Location: _____

Purpose of Test: _____

Retest Score, if Applicable: _____ Retest Date: _____

Deadline to Reapply for Next Testing: _____

Test Cost: _____ Additional Fees: _____

Contact Person:_____ Phone: _____

FORM S303

VOCATIONAL/PROFESSIONAL TRAINING

Name: _____

Name of School/Training Center: _____

Address:_____ Phone: _____

Training Dates: _____ to_____ Total Training Hours: _____

Purpose: _____

Skills/Equipment Learned: _____

Company Sponsor (if applicable): _____

Certificates/Awards Received: _____

Name of School/Training Center: _____

Address:_____ Phone: _____

Training Dates: _____ to_____ Total Training Hours: _____

Purpose: _____

Skills/Equipment Learned: _____

Company Sponsor (if applicable): _____

Certificates/Awards Received: _____

Name of School/Training Center: _____

Address:_____ Phone: _____

Training Dates: _____ to_____ Total Training Hours: _____

Purpose: _____

Skills/Equipment Learned: _____

Company Sponsor (if applicable): _____

Certificates/Awards Received: _____

Section 4
Health Records

Form C401	**Chart of Child's Growth** – Measures a child's height and weight growth
Form D401	**Daily Calorie Count Summary** – Charts daily caloric intake
Form D402	**Dental Visit Log** – Lists dental visits made
Form F401	**Fitness Training Schedule** – Plans your weekly workout routine
Form H401	**Health Insurance** – Provides important health insurance policy information
Form H402	**Hospitalization Record** – Summary of hospital stays
Form L401	**Life Insurance Fact Sheet** – Details information on life insurance policies
Form L402	**Listing of Medical Services** – Lists phone numbers of frequently called medical service providers
Form M401	**Medical Expense Ledger** – Charts health care expenses
Form O401	**Optical Record** – Updates eyecare information
Form P401	**Personal Health Record** – Listing of all medical visits and personal health information
Form R401	**Records of Birth** – Lists vital birth data
Form R402	**Registry of Prescriptions** – Log of prescription drug medication
Form R403	**Routine Checkups** – Compiles information on routine medical and dental checkups
Form S401	**Schedule of Vaccinations** – Reference guide for all vaccinations
Form W401	**Weight Tracking Guide** – Charts daily or weekly weight changes

CHART OF CHILD'S GROWTH

Name of Child: _____ Date of Birth: _____

Date	Age	Height	Weight	Comments
_____	_____	_____	_____	_____
_____	_____	_____	_____	_____
_____	_____	_____	_____	_____
_____	_____	_____	_____	_____
_____	_____	_____	_____	_____
_____	_____	_____	_____	_____
_____	_____	_____	_____	_____
_____	_____	_____	_____	_____
_____	_____	_____	_____	_____
_____	_____	_____	_____	_____
_____	_____	_____	_____	_____
_____	_____	_____	_____	_____
_____	_____	_____	_____	_____
_____	_____	_____	_____	_____
_____	_____	_____	_____	_____
_____	_____	_____	_____	_____
_____	_____	_____	_____	_____
_____	_____	_____	_____	_____
_____	_____	_____	_____	_____
_____	_____	_____	_____	_____
_____	_____	_____	_____	_____
_____	_____	_____	_____	_____

DAILY CALORIE COUNT SUMMARY

Name of Calorie Counter: _____

Day: _____ Date: _____ Weight: _____

	Menu	Calories

Breakfast: _____ _____

                     _____ _____

                     _____ _____

                     _____ _____

Lunch: _____ _____

                     _____ _____

                     _____ _____

                     _____ _____

Dinner: _____ _____

                     _____ _____

                     _____ _____

                     _____ _____

Snacks: _____ _____

                     _____ _____

                     _____ _____

Total Calories Consumed: _____

Total Calories Allowed: _____

Net +/-: _____

FORM D401

DENTAL VISIT LOG

Name of Patient:_____ Year: _____

Dentist:_____ Phone:_____

Address: _____

Orthodontist:_____ Phone:_____

Address: _____

Date	Reason for Visit/Treatment	Cost
_____	_____	$ _____
_____	_____	$ _____
_____	_____	$ _____
_____	_____	$ _____
_____	_____	$ _____
_____	_____	$ _____
_____	_____	$ _____
_____	_____	$ _____
_____	_____	$ _____
_____	_____	$ _____
_____	_____	$ _____
_____	_____	$ _____
_____	_____	$ _____
_____	_____	$ _____
_____	_____	$ _____
_____	_____	$ _____
_____	_____	$ _____
_____	_____	$ _____
_____	_____	$ _____

Total Annual Dental Cost $ _____

FITNESS TRAINING SCHEDULE

Name: _____

Name of Fitness Center: _____ Phone: _____

Sunday (- -)

Workout Planned: _____

Workout Completed: _____

Monday (- -)

Workout Planned: _____

Workout Completed: _____

Tuesday (- -)

Workout Planned: _____

Workout Completed: _____

Wednesday (- -)

Workout Planned: _____

Workout Completed: _____

Thursday (- -)

Workout Planned: _____

Workout Completed: _____

Friday (- -)

Workout Planned: _____

Workout Completed: _____

Saturday (- -)

Workout Planned: _____

Workout Completed: _____

FORM F401

HEALTH INSURANCE

Name of Insured: _____ Date: _____

Insurance Company: _____

Policy #:_____ Premium: $ _____ per _____

Premium Due: _____ Type of Policy: _____

Agent: _____

Address: _____

Phone: _____ Location of Policy: _____

_____

Secondary Coverage: _____

_____

_____

_____

Terms of Contract: _____

_____

_____

_____

Exceptions: _____

_____

_____

_____

Additional Information: _____

_____

_____

_____

_____

HOSPITALIZATION RECORD

Name: _____

Dates of Hospitalization: _____ to _____

Name of Hospital: _____ Phone: _____

Location: _____

Condition: _____

_____

Treatment: _____

Hospitalization Costs: _____

Attending Physician: _____

Comments: _____

_____

Name: _____

Dates of Hospitalization: _____ to _____

Name of Hospital: _____ Phone: _____

Location: _____

Condition: _____

_____

Treatment: _____

Hospitalization Costs: _____

Attending Physician: _____

Comments: _____

_____

FORM H402

LIFE INSURANCE FACT SHEET

Name of Insured: _____ Date: _____

Policy Holder: _____ Policy #:_____

Name of Insurance Company: _____

Agent:_____ Type of Policy: _____

Address:_____ Phone : _____

Anniversary Date of Policy: _____

Location of Policy: _____

Primary Beneficiary:_____

Secondary Beneficiary:_____

Face: $ _____ Premium: $_____ per _____

Other Important Information:_____

_____

_____

_____

_____

_____

_____

_____

_____

_____

_____

_____

_____

_____

LISTING OF MEDICAL SERVICES

Name: _____

Physician: _____ Phone: _____
    Address: _____

Gynecologist: _____ Phone: _____
    Address: _____

Optometrist: _____ Phone: _____
    Address: _____

Dentist:_____ Phone: _____
    Address: _____

Orthodontist:_____ Phone: _____
    Address: _____

Veterinarian_____ Phone: _____
    Address: _____

Hospital: _____ Phone: _____
    Address: _____

Pharmacy: _____ Phone: _____
    Address: _____

Other/Specialists: _____ Phone: _____
    Address: _____

Other/Specialists: _____ Phone: _____
    Address: _____

Other/Specialists: _____ Phone: _____
    Address: _____

FORM L402

MEDICAL EXPENSE LEDGER

Name:_____ Year:_____

Date	Service Provider	Cost	Third-Party Paid (✓)	Net Expense
_____	_____	$ _____	_____	$ _____
_____	_____	$ _____	_____	$ _____
_____	_____	$ _____	_____	$ _____
_____	_____	$ _____	_____	$ _____
_____	_____	$ _____	_____	$ _____
_____	_____	$ _____	_____	$ _____
_____	_____	$ _____	_____	$ _____
_____	_____	$ _____	_____	$ _____
_____	_____	$ _____	_____	$ _____
_____	_____	$ _____	_____	$ _____
_____	_____	$ _____	_____	$ _____
_____	_____	$ _____	_____	$ _____
_____	_____	$ _____	_____	$ _____
_____	_____	$ _____	_____	$ _____
	Annual Total:	$ _____		$ _____

OPTICAL RECORD

Name:_____ Date: _____

Physician: _____ Phone : _____

Address: _____

Prescription:

	O.S.		O.D.
Sphere	_____	/	_____
Cylinder	_____	/	_____
Axis	_____	/	_____
Add	_____	/	_____

Comments/Information: _____

_____

_____

_____

Name:_____ Date: _____

Physician: _____ Phone : _____

Address: _____

Prescription:

	O.S.		O.D.
Sphere	_____	/	_____
Cylinder	_____	/	_____
Axis	_____	/	_____
Add	_____	/	_____

Comments/Information: _____

_____

_____

_____

FORM O401

PERSONAL HEALTH RECORD

Name: _____

Date: _____ Purpose of Visit/Symptoms: _____

_____

Treatment/Diagnosis: _____

_____

Physician: _____ Phone: _____

Date: _____ Purpose of Visit/Symptoms: _____

_____

Treatment/Diagnosis: _____

_____

Physician: _____ Phone: _____

Date: _____ Purpose of Visit/Symptoms: _____

_____

Treatment/Diagnosis: _____

_____

Physician: _____ Phone: _____

Prior Health Problems: _____

_____

_____

Allergies: _____

_____

_____

Family History of Disease: _____

_____

_____

RECORDS OF BIRTH

Name: _____ Sex: _____

Parents' Names: _____

Birth Date: _____ Time of Birth: _____

Place of Birth: _____

Name of Hospital: _____ Phone: _____

Address: _____

Attending Physician: _____

Birthweight: _____ Length: _____

Hair Color: _____ Eye Color: _____ Blood Type: _____

Namesake: _____

Birthmarks/Distinguishing Traits: _____

_____

Relevant Information: _____

_____

_____

_____

_____

_____

_____

_____

_____

_____

_____

_____

_____

FORM R401

REGISTRY OF PRESCRIPTIONS

Name: _____

Name of Drug: _____ Rx #: _____

Date Prescribed: _____ Exp. Date: _____

Physician: _____ Phone: _____

Pharmacy: _____ Phone: _____

Comments: _____

_____

_____

Name: _____

Name of Drug: _____ Rx #: _____

Date Prescribed: _____ Exp. Date: _____

Physician: _____ Phone: _____

Pharmacy: _____ Phone: _____

Comments: _____

_____

_____

Name: _____

Name of Drug: _____ Rx #: _____

Date Prescribed: _____ Exp. Date: _____

Physician: _____ Phone: _____

Pharmacy: _____ Phone: _____

Comments: _____

_____

_____

ROUTINE CHECKUPS

Dental:

Patient Name	Date Last Checkup	Dentist	Next Checkup Due Date	Phone

Medical:

Patient Name	Date Last Checkup	Doctor	Next Checkup Due Date	Phone

FORM   R403

SCHEDULE OF VACCINATIONS

Name: _____

Vaccinated Against: _____ Date: _____

Name of Clinic and/or Physician: _____

Phone: _____ Booster/Revaccination Date: _____

Location of Stamped Certificate: _____

Other Information: _____

Name: _____

Vaccinated Against: _____ Date: _____

Name of Clinic and/or Physician: _____

Phone: _____ Booster/Revaccination Date: _____

Location of Stamped Certificate: _____

Other Information: _____

Name: _____

Vaccinated Against: _____ Date: _____

Name of Clinic and/or Physician: _____

Phone: _____ Booster/Revaccination Date: _____

Location of Stamped Certificate: _____

Other Information: _____

Name: _____

Vaccinated Against: _____ Date: _____

Name of Clinic and/or Physician: _____

Phone: _____ Booster/Revaccination Date: _____

Location of Stamped Certificate: _____

Other Information: _____

WEIGHT TRACKING GUIDE

Name: _____

Date	Day	Weight	Comments
____	____	____	____
____	____	____	____
____	____	____	____
____	____	____	____
____	____	____	____
____	____	____	____
____	____	____	____
____	____	____	____
____	____	____	____
____	____	____	____
____	____	____	____
____	____	____	____
____	____	____	____
____	____	____	____
____	____	____	____
____	____	____	____
____	____	____	____
____	____	____	____
____	____	____	____
____	____	____	____
____	____	____	____
____	____	____	____

FORM W401

Section 5
Investments/Financial Records

Form A501   **Accounts Receivable** – Lists account payments due

Form A502   **Additional Valuable Assets** – Organizes personal valuable assets owned

Form A503   **Annual Expense Summary** – Applies living expenses to yearly household income

Form B501   **Bank Account Record** – Listing of various banking accounts owned

Form B502   **Bond Purchase Ledger** – Details bond purchases made

Form C501   **Certificates of Deposit** – Provides essential banking and financial information on certificates of deposit owned

Form C502   **Certificates of Deposit List** – Tracks profits based on interest rates for certificates of deposit owned

Form C503   **Charge Account Summary** – Record of outstanding balances, interest rates and expected monthly payments on all charge accounts owned

Form C504   **Charitable Contributions** – Listing of monetary donations during a specific time period

Form C505   **Corporate/Municipal Bonds Record** – Record of various bond types owned and maturity dates

Form C506   **Credit Card Ledger** – Gives pertinent information on all credit cards owned

Form D501   **Deposit Box Contents Log** – Inventory of possessions held in safety deposit box

Form D502   **Disability Insurance Record** – Lists various disability insurance policies

Form E501   **Expense Reimbursement Form** – Keeps record of expenses incurred for expected reimbursement

Form H501   **History of Loan Payments** – Catalogs loan payments made by debtor and corresponding balance of entire loan

Form I501   **Insured Property List** – Lists value of all insured property owned

Form I502   **Interest Payments** – Tracks interest payments made on a particular charge account

Form I503   **Investment Gains and Losses** – Charts all profits and losses incurred from financial investments

Form I504   **Investment Securities** – Log of investment securities purchased

Form K501   **Keoghs and IRAs** – Provides essential information on keoghs and individual retirement accounts owned

Form L501   **Loan Identification Form** – Details types of loans oustanding

Form M501   **Money Market Accounts** – Listing of short-term system for providing loanable funds

Form M502   **Monthly Expense Summary** – Lists monthly expenses against monthly income from employment and other financial sources

Form O501   **Outstanding Debts** – Lists all current debts owed

Form P501   **Pension Contribution Log** – Lists monthly pension contributions and withdrawals

Form P502   **Personal Financial Statement** – States personal net worth after deducting debts from assets

Form P503   **Philanthropic Donations** – Lists all donations made to philanthropic groups and the value of goods donated

Form P504   **Precious Metal Record** – Log of precious metals investments

Form P505   **Property and Liability Insurance Coverage** – Specifies insurance policies covering property and personal liability

Form R501	**Record of Income** – Charts all wages and deductions from weekly, quarterly and annual employment
Form R502	**Retirement Expenses** – Helps plan finances following retirement
Form R503	**Returns on Investments** – Charts investment income amounts received
Form S501	**Sale of Bonds** – Logs all bond sales made
Form S502	**Savings Bonds Collection** – Lists all savings bonds owned and price paid
Form S503	**Savings/Checking Account Record** – Lists all savings and checking accounts owned
Form S504	**Social Security Registry** – Charts social security funds contributed and date benefits begin
Form S505	**Stock Price Fluctuations** – Follows gains or losses of stocks owned
Form S506	**Stock Purchases** – Keeps record of all stocks bought
Form S507	**Stock Sales** – Keeps record of all stocks sold
Form T501	**Tally of Day-by-Day Closing Balances** – Lists closing prices and account value on certain securities
Form T502	**Tax Record Finder** – Locates all materials and documents for tax preparation
Form U501	**Unit Investment Trusts** – Log of trust transactions
Form U502	**U.S Savings/Treasury Bonds Registry** – Lists savings and treasury bonds purchased and maturity dates
Form W501	**Wills and Trusts** – Provides essential information on wills and trusts established
Form Z501	**Zero Coupon Bonds Registry** – Records purchased zero coupon bonds, price, interest rate and date of maturity

ACCOUNTS RECEIVABLE

Name: _____

Account Name	Account #	Amount Due	Date Received	Payment Amount	Next Due Date
_____	_____	$ _____	_____	$ _____	_____
_____	_____	$ _____	_____	$ _____	_____
_____	_____	$ _____	_____	$ _____	_____
_____	_____	$ _____	_____	$ _____	_____
_____	_____	$ _____	_____	$ _____	_____
_____	_____	$ _____	_____	$ _____	_____
_____	_____	$ _____	_____	$ _____	_____
_____	_____	$ _____	_____	$ _____	_____
_____	_____	$ _____	_____	$ _____	_____
_____	_____	$ _____	_____	$ _____	_____
_____	_____	$ _____	_____	$ _____	_____
_____	_____	$ _____	_____	$ _____	_____
_____	_____	$ _____	_____	$ _____	_____
_____	_____	$ _____	_____	$ _____	_____
_____	_____	$ _____	_____	$ _____	_____
_____	_____	$ _____	_____	$ _____	_____
_____	_____	$ _____	_____	$ _____	_____
_____	_____	$ _____	_____	$ _____	_____
_____	_____	$ _____	_____	$ _____	_____
_____	_____	$ _____	_____	$ _____	_____

Total Due: $ _____   **Total Received:** $ _____

ADDITIONAL VALUABLE ASSETS

Name: _____

Valuable Asset:_____

Asset Description: _____

_____

Purchase Date: _____ Purchase Price: $ _____

Present Value: $ _____ Date Sold: _____ Price Sold: $_____

Location of Asset and/or Records:_____

Additional Information: _____

Name: _____

Valuable Asset:_____

Asset Description: _____

_____

Purchase Date: _____ Purchase Price: $ _____

Present Value: $ _____ Date Sold: _____ Price Sold: $_____

Location of Asset and/or Records:_____

Additional Information: _____

Name: _____

Valuable Asset:_____

Asset Description: _____

_____

Purchase Date: _____ Purchase Price: $ _____

Present Value: $ _____ Date Sold: _____ Price Sold: $_____

Location of Asset and/or Records:_____

Additional Information: _____

FORM A502

ANNUAL EXPENSE SUMMARY

Name:_____ Year:_____

INCOME	Last Year	This Year	Next Year
Salaries	$_____	$_____	$_____
Commissions/Bonuses	_____	_____	_____
Interest	_____	_____	_____
Alimony	_____	_____	_____
Child Support	_____	_____	_____
Rent	_____	_____	_____
Property Sales	_____	_____	_____
Royalties	_____	_____	_____
Security Sales	_____	_____	_____
Trust Fund	_____	_____	_____
Annuities	_____	_____	_____
Pensions	_____	_____	_____
Social Security	_____	_____	_____
Other:_____	_____	_____	_____
Total Income	$_____	$_____	$_____
TAXES			
Property Taxes	$_____	$_____	$_____
Social Security	_____	_____	_____
State/City Income Tax	_____	_____	_____
Federal Income Tax	_____	_____	_____
Total Tax Expenditures	$_____	$_____	$_____
LIVING EXPENSES			
Mortgage/Rent	$_____	$_____	$_____
Food	_____	_____	_____
Utilities: Electric	_____	_____	_____
Heat	_____	_____	_____
Water	_____	_____	_____
Phone	_____	_____	_____
Other:_____	_____	_____	_____
Credit Cards:_____	_____	_____	_____
	_____	_____	_____
Insurance: Health	_____	_____	_____
Life	_____	_____	_____
Auto	_____	_____	_____
Loans:_____	_____	_____	_____
Personal/Health Care	_____	_____	_____
Clothing/Maint.	_____	_____	_____
Child Care	_____	_____	_____
Education	_____	_____	_____
Home Maintenance	_____	_____	_____
Membership Fees	_____	_____	_____
Entertainment/Rec.	_____	_____	_____
Contributions	_____	_____	_____
Investments	_____	_____	_____
Savings	_____	_____	_____
Auto: Maintenance	_____	_____	_____
Loan	_____	_____	_____
Gas	_____	_____	_____
Legal Expenses	_____	_____	_____
Other:_____	_____	_____	_____
Total Living Expenses	$_____	$_____	$_____

BANK ACCOUNT RECORD

Name: _____

Name of Bank	Date	Type of Account	Account #	Balance	Interest Rate
_____	_____	_____	_____	$ _____	_____
_____	_____	_____	_____	$ _____	_____
_____	_____	_____	_____	$ _____	_____
_____	_____	_____	_____	$ _____	_____
_____	_____	_____	_____	$ _____	_____
_____	_____	_____	_____	$ _____	_____
_____	_____	_____	_____	$ _____	_____
_____	_____	_____	_____	$ _____	_____
_____	_____	_____	_____	$ _____	_____
_____	_____	_____	_____	$ _____	_____
_____	_____	_____	_____	$ _____	_____
_____	_____	_____	_____	$ _____	_____
_____	_____	_____	_____	$ _____	_____
_____	_____	_____	_____	$ _____	_____
_____	_____	_____	_____	$ _____	_____
_____	_____	_____	_____	$ _____	_____
_____	_____	_____	_____	$ _____	_____
_____	_____	_____	_____	$ _____	_____
_____	_____	_____	_____	$ _____	_____
_____	_____	_____	_____	$ _____	_____
_____	_____	_____	_____	$ _____	_____
_____	_____	_____	_____	$ _____	_____
_____	_____	_____	_____	$ _____	_____

FORM B501

BOND PURCHASE LEDGER

Purchaser's Name:_____ Date: _____

Purchase Period:_____ to _____

Type of Bond:_____ Issued by:_____

Date of Purchase: _____ Face Value:_____

Broker:_____ Purchase Price: $ _____ Coupon Rate: _____

Type of Bond:_____ Issued by:_____

Date of Purchase: _____ Face Value:_____

Broker:_____ Purchase Price: $ _____ Coupon Rate: _____

Type of Bond:_____ Issued by:_____

Date of Purchase: _____ Face Value:_____

Broker:_____ Purchase Price: $ _____ Coupon Rate: _____

Type of Bond:_____ Issued by:_____

Date of Purchase: _____ Face Value:_____

Broker:_____ Purchase Price: $ _____ Coupon Rate: _____

Type of Bond:_____ Issued by:_____

Date of Purchase: _____ Face Value:_____

Broker:_____ Purchase Price: $ _____ Coupon Rate: _____

Type of Bond:_____ Issued by:_____

Date of Purchase: _____ Face Value:_____

Broker:_____ Purchase Price: $ _____ Coupon Rate: _____

CERTIFICATES OF DEPOSIT

Name: _____

CD Account #: _____

Purchase Date: _____ Principal: $_____

Interest Rate: _____ Maturity Rate: _____

Banking Institution: _____

Address: _____

Contact: _____ Phone: _____

Certificate/Book Location: _____

Additional Details: _____

_____

_____

_____

Name: _____

CD Account #: _____

Purchase Date: _____ Principal: $_____

Interest Rate: _____ Maturity Rate: _____

Banking Institution: _____

Address: _____

Contact: _____ Phone: _____

Certificate/Book Location: _____

Additional Details: _____

_____

_____

_____

FORM C501

CERTIFICATES OF DEPOSIT LIST

Name: _____

Certificate	Date Purchased	Interest Rate	Profit Margin
_____	_____	_____	_____
_____	_____	_____	_____
_____	_____	_____	_____
_____	_____	_____	_____
_____	_____	_____	_____
_____	_____	_____	_____
_____	_____	_____	_____
_____	_____	_____	_____
_____	_____	_____	_____
_____	_____	_____	_____
_____	_____	_____	_____
_____	_____	_____	_____
_____	_____	_____	_____
_____	_____	_____	_____
_____	_____	_____	_____
_____	_____	_____	_____
_____	_____	_____	_____
_____	_____	_____	_____
_____	_____	_____	_____
_____	_____	_____	_____
_____	_____	_____	_____

CHARGE ACCOUNT SUMMARY

Name: _____

Charge Account:_____ #: _____
Authorized Users: _____
Interest Rate: _____
Date: _____ Payment: $ _____ Balance: $ _____

Charge Account:_____ #: _____
Authorized Users: _____
Interest Rate: _____
Date: _____ Payment: $ _____ Balance: $ _____

Charge Account:_____ #: _____
Authorized Users: _____
Interest Rate: _____
Date: _____ Payment: $ _____ Balance: $ _____

Charge Account:_____ #: _____
Authorized Users: _____
Interest Rate: _____
Date: _____ Payment: $ _____ Balance: $ _____

Charge Account:_____ #: _____
Authorized Users: _____
Interest Rate: _____
Date: _____ Payment: $ _____ Balance: $ _____

FORM C503

CHARITABLE CONTRIBUTIONS

Name:_____ Date: _____

Institution: _____ Donation Period: _____ to _____

Donor	Date	Donation
_____	_____	$ _____
_____	_____	$ _____
_____	_____	$ _____
_____	_____	$ _____
_____	_____	$ _____
_____	_____	$ _____
_____	_____	$ _____
_____	_____	$ _____
_____	_____	$ _____
_____	_____	$ _____
_____	_____	$ _____
_____	_____	$ _____
_____	_____	$ _____
_____	_____	$ _____
_____	_____	$ _____
_____	_____	$ _____
_____	_____	$ _____
_____	_____	$ _____
_____	_____	$ _____
_____	_____	$ _____
_____	_____	$ _____
_____	_____	$ _____
	Total:	$ _____

CORPORATE/MUNICIPAL BONDS RECORD

Name: _____

Type of Bond	Series #	Date Purchased	Purchase Price	Date of Maturity
_____	_____	_____	$ _____	_____
_____	_____	_____	$ _____	_____
_____	_____	_____	$ _____	_____
_____	_____	_____	$ _____	_____
_____	_____	_____	$ _____	_____
_____	_____	_____	$ _____	_____
_____	_____	_____	$ _____	_____
_____	_____	_____	$ _____	_____
_____	_____	_____	$ _____	_____
_____	_____	_____	$ _____	_____
_____	_____	_____	$ _____	_____
_____	_____	_____	$ _____	_____
_____	_____	_____	$ _____	_____
_____	_____	_____	$ _____	_____
_____	_____	_____	$ _____	_____
_____	_____	_____	$ _____	_____
_____	_____	_____	$ _____	_____
_____	_____	_____	$ _____	_____
_____	_____	_____	$ _____	_____
_____	_____	_____	$ _____	_____
_____	_____	_____	$ _____	_____
_____	_____	_____	$ _____	_____
			$ _____	

FORM C505

CREDIT CARD LEDGER

Name: _____

Credit Card: _____ Annual Fee: $_____

Account #: _____ Expiration Date: _____

Authorized Credit Limit: $_____ Interest Rate: _____

Lost Card/Customer Service #: _____

Authorized Users: _____

Credit Card: _____ Annual Fee: $_____

Account #: _____ Expiration Date: _____

Authorized Credit Limit: $_____ Interest Rate: _____

Lost Card/Customer Service #: _____

Authorized Users: _____

Credit Card: _____ Annual Fee: $_____

Account #: _____ Expiration Date: _____

Authorized Credit Limit: $_____ Interest Rate: _____

Lost Card/Customer Service #: _____

Authorized Users: _____

Credit Card: _____ Annual Fee: $_____

Account #: _____ Expiration Date: _____

Authorized Credit Limit: $_____ Interest Rate: _____

Lost Card/Customer Service #: _____

Authorized Users: _____

DEPOSIT BOX CONTENTS LOG

Name: _____

Safety Deposit Box Location: _____

Address: _____

_____

Box #: _____ Location of Key: _____

Owners/Keyholders: _____

_____

Date	Inventory of Box Contents	Value
_____	_____	$ _____
_____	_____	$ _____
_____	_____	$ _____
_____	_____	$ _____
_____	_____	$ _____
_____	_____	$ _____
_____	_____	$ _____
_____	_____	$ _____
_____	_____	$ _____
_____	_____	$ _____
_____	_____	$ _____
_____	_____	$ _____
_____	_____	$ _____
_____	_____	$ _____
_____	_____	$ _____
_____	_____	$ _____
_____	_____	$ _____
_____	_____	$ _____
_____	_____	$ _____

Total: $ _____

FORM D501

DISABILITY INSURANCE RECORD

Name of Insured: _____

Policy #1

Company: _____

Policy #: _____ Type: _____

Benefits: _____

_____

Expires: _____ Annual Premium: $ _____ Due: _____

Policy #2

Company: _____

Policy #: _____ Type: _____

Benefits: _____

_____

Expires: _____ Annual Premium: $ _____ Due: _____

Policy #3

Company: _____

Policy #: _____ Type: _____

Benefits: _____

_____

Expires: _____ Annual Premium: $ _____ Due: _____

Policy #4

Company: _____

Policy #: _____ Type: _____

Benefits: _____

_____

Expires: _____ Annual Premium: $ _____ Due: _____

EXPENSE REIMBURSEMENT FORM

Name: _____

Item	Cost	Purchase Date	Reimbursement Date
_____	$ _____	_____	_____
_____	$ _____	_____	_____
_____	$ _____	_____	_____
_____	$ _____	_____	_____
_____	$ _____	_____	_____
_____	$ _____	_____	_____
_____	$ _____	_____	_____
_____	$ _____	_____	_____
_____	$ _____	_____	_____
_____	$ _____	_____	_____
_____	$ _____	_____	_____
_____	$ _____	_____	_____
_____	$ _____	_____	_____
_____	$ _____	_____	_____
_____	$ _____	_____	_____
_____	$ _____	_____	_____
_____	$ _____	_____	_____
_____	$ _____	_____	_____
_____	$ _____	_____	_____
_____	$ _____	_____	_____
_____	$ _____	_____	_____

Total: $ _____

FORM E501

HISTORY OF LOAN PAYMENTS

Loan Payer: _____   Loan Recipient: _____

Terms: _____

Date Due	Date Paid	Amount	Balance
_____	_____	$ _____	$ _____
_____	_____	$ _____	$ _____
_____	_____	$ _____	$ _____
_____	_____	$ _____	$ _____
_____	_____	$ _____	$ _____
_____	_____	$ _____	$ _____
_____	_____	$ _____	$ _____
_____	_____	$ _____	$ _____
_____	_____	$ _____	$ _____
_____	_____	$ _____	$ _____
_____	_____	$ _____	$ _____
_____	_____	$ _____	$ _____
_____	_____	$ _____	$ _____
_____	_____	$ _____	$ _____
_____	_____	$ _____	$ _____
_____	_____	$ _____	$ _____
_____	_____	$ _____	$ _____
_____	_____	$ _____	$ _____
_____	_____	$ _____	$ _____
_____	_____	$ _____	$ _____
_____	_____	$ _____	$ _____
_____	_____	$ _____	$ _____
_____	_____	$ _____	$ _____

INSURED PROPERTY LIST

Name: _____

Insured Property Description	Policy/ Rider	Insured Value
_____	_____	$_____
_____	_____	$_____
_____	_____	$_____
_____	_____	$_____
_____	_____	$_____
_____	_____	$_____
_____	_____	$_____
_____	_____	$_____
_____	_____	$_____
_____	_____	$_____
_____	_____	$_____
_____	_____	$_____
_____	_____	$_____
_____	_____	$_____
_____	_____	$_____
_____	_____	$_____
_____	_____	$_____
_____	_____	$_____
_____	_____	$_____
_____	_____	$_____
_____	_____	$_____
_____	_____	$_____

FORM I501

INTEREST PAYMENTS

Name: _____

For the Month Of: _____ 19 _____

Paid to	Date	Total	Principal	Interest
_____	_____	$ _____	$ _____	$ _____
_____	_____	$ _____	$ _____	$ _____
_____	_____	$ _____	$ _____	$ _____
_____	_____	$ _____	$ _____	$ _____
_____	_____	$ _____	$ _____	$ _____
_____	_____	$ _____	$ _____	$ _____
_____	_____	$ _____	$ _____	$ _____
_____	_____	$ _____	$ _____	$ _____
_____	_____	$ _____	$ _____	$ _____
_____	_____	$ _____	$ _____	$ _____
_____	_____	$ _____	$ _____	$ _____
_____	_____	$ _____	$ _____	$ _____
_____	_____	$ _____	$ _____	$ _____
_____	_____	$ _____	$ _____	$ _____
_____	_____	$ _____	$ _____	$ _____
_____	_____	$ _____	$ _____	$ _____
_____	_____	$ _____	$ _____	$ _____
_____	_____	$ _____	$ _____	$ _____
_____	_____	$ _____	$ _____	$ _____
_____	_____	$ _____	$ _____	$ _____
_____	_____	$ _____	$ _____	$ _____
_____	_____	$ _____	$ _____	$ _____
_____	_____	$ _____	$ _____	$ _____

Monthly Totals: $ _____ $ _____ $ _____

INVESTMENT GAINS AND LOSSES

Name: _____

Time Period Covered: _____ to_____

Investment Description	Price Paid	Sales Price	Gain or Loss	Date Purchased	Date Sold
_____	$ _____	$_____	$_____	_____	_____
_____	$ _____	$_____	$_____	_____	_____
_____	$ _____	$_____	$_____	_____	_____
_____	$ _____	$_____	$_____	_____	_____
_____	$ _____	$_____	$_____	_____	_____
_____	$ _____	$_____	$_____	_____	_____
_____	$ _____	$_____	$_____	_____	_____
_____	$ _____	$_____	$_____	_____	_____
_____	$ _____	$_____	$_____	_____	_____
_____	$ _____	$_____	$_____	_____	_____
_____	$ _____	$_____	$_____	_____	_____
_____	$ _____	$_____	$_____	_____	_____
_____	$ _____	$_____	$_____	_____	_____
_____	$ _____	$_____	$_____	_____	_____
_____	$ _____	$_____	$_____	_____	_____
_____	$ _____	$_____	$_____	_____	_____
_____	$ _____	$_____	$_____	_____	_____
_____	$ _____	$_____	$_____	_____	_____
_____	$ _____	$_____	$_____	_____	_____
_____	$ _____	$_____	$_____	_____	_____
_____	$ _____	$_____	$_____	_____	_____

FORM I503

INVESTMENT SECURITIES

Name: _____

Security Description	# Shares	Purchase Date	Maturity Date	Purchase Price	Current Value
_____	_____	_____	_____	$_____	$_____
_____	_____	_____	_____	$_____	$_____
_____	_____	_____	_____	$_____	$_____
_____	_____	_____	_____	$_____	$_____
_____	_____	_____	_____	$_____	$_____
_____	_____	_____	_____	$_____	$_____
_____	_____	_____	_____	$_____	$_____
_____	_____	_____	_____	$_____	$_____
_____	_____	_____	_____	$_____	$_____
_____	_____	_____	_____	$_____	$_____
_____	_____	_____	_____	$_____	$_____
_____	_____	_____	_____	$_____	$_____
_____	_____	_____	_____	$_____	$_____
_____	_____	_____	_____	$_____	$_____
_____	_____	_____	_____	$_____	$_____
_____	_____	_____	_____	$_____	$_____
_____	_____	_____	_____	$_____	$_____
_____	_____	_____	_____	$_____	$_____
_____	_____	_____	_____	$_____	$_____
_____	_____	_____	_____	$_____	$_____
_____	_____	_____	_____	$_____	$_____
_____	_____	_____	_____	$_____	$_____

KEOGHS AND IRAS

Name: _____

Plan Description: _____ Account #: _____

Date Account Opened: _____ Current Balance: $_____

Where Invested: _____

Account Supervisor: _____ Phone: _____

Address: _____

_____

Trustee/Beneficiary: _____

Document Location: _____

Additional Information: _____

_____

_____

Name: _____

Plan Description: _____ Account #: _____

Date Account Opened: _____ Current Balance: $_____

Where Invested: _____

Account Supervisor: _____ Phone: _____

Address: _____

_____

Trustee/Beneficiary: _____

Document Location: _____

Additional Information: _____

_____

_____

FORM K501

LOAN IDENTIFICATION FORM

Name: _____

Loan Type: _____

  Account #: _____ Principal: $ _____

  Interest Rate: _____ Date Borrowed: _____ Term of Loan: _____

  Monthly Payment: $ _____ Date Due: _____

  Date Payments Begin: _____

  Lender: _____

  Address: _____

  Contact: _____ Phone: _____

  Additional Information: _____

  _____

  _____

Loan Type: _____

  Account #: _____ Principal: $ _____

  Interest Rate: _____ Date Borrowed: _____ Term of Loan: _____

  Monthly Payment: $ _____ Date Due: _____

  Date Payments Begin: _____

  Lender: _____

  Address: _____

  Contact: _____ Phone: _____

  Additional Information: _____

  _____

  _____

MONEY MARKET ACCOUNTS

Name: _____

Name of Fund: _____ Account #: _____

Name of Firm: _____

Contact Name: _____ Phone: _____

Date Account Established: _____ Initial Investment: _____

Date of Contribution	Amount of Contribution	Balance
_____	$_____	$_____
_____	$_____	$_____
_____	$_____	$_____
_____	$_____	$_____
_____	$_____	$_____
_____	$_____	$_____
_____	$_____	$_____
_____	$_____	$_____
_____	$_____	$_____
_____	$_____	$_____
_____	$_____	$_____
_____	$_____	$_____
_____	$_____	$_____
_____	$_____	$_____
_____	$_____	$_____
_____	$_____	$_____
_____	$_____	$_____
_____	$_____	$_____
_____	$_____	$_____

FORM M502

MONTHLY EXPENSE SUMMARY

Name:_____ Month:_____ Year:_____

Income

Salaries	$_____
Commissions/Bonuses	_____
Interest	_____
Dividends	_____
Alimony	_____
Child Support	_____
Rents	_____
Property Sales	_____
Royalties	_____
Security	_____
Sales	_____
Trust Funds	_____
Annuities	_____
Pensions	_____
Social Security	_____
Other: _____	_____
_____	_____
_____	_____
_____	_____
_____	_____
Total Income	$_____

Expenses

Mortgage/Rent	$_____
Utilities: Heat	_____
Elec.	_____
Water	_____
Phone	_____
Other:_____	_____
Home Maintenance	_____
Food	_____
Auto: Loan	_____
Maint.	_____
Gas	_____
Credit Cards:	_____
_____	_____
_____	_____
_____	_____
Insurance: Life	_____
Auto	_____
Health	_____
Loans:	_____
	_____
Clothing/Maint.	_____
Personal/Health Care	
Child Care	_____
Education	_____
Membership Fees	_____
Entertainment/Rec.	_____
Contributions	_____
Property Tax	_____
Income Tax	_____
Investments/Savings	_____
Legal Expenses	_____
Other:_____	_____
_____	_____
_____	_____
Total Expenses	$_____

OUTSTANDING DEBTS

Borrower's Name: _____ Date: _____

Lender	Phone	Reason for Loan	Debt	Date Due
_____	_____	_____	$_____	_____
_____	_____	_____	$_____	_____
_____	_____	_____	$_____	_____
_____	_____	_____	$_____	_____
_____	_____	_____	$_____	_____
_____	_____	_____	$_____	_____
_____	_____	_____	$_____	_____
_____	_____	_____	$_____	_____
_____	_____	_____	$_____	_____
_____	_____	_____	$_____	_____
_____	_____	_____	$_____	_____
_____	_____	_____	$_____	_____
_____	_____	_____	$_____	_____
_____	_____	_____	$_____	_____
_____	_____	_____	$_____	_____
_____	_____	_____	$_____	_____
_____	_____	_____	$_____	_____
_____	_____	_____	$_____	_____
_____	_____	_____	$_____	_____
_____	_____	_____	$_____	_____
_____	_____	_____	$_____	_____
_____	_____	_____	$_____	_____

Total: $_____

FORM O501

PENSION CONTRIBUTION LOG

Contributor Name: _____

Investment Type: _____

Year: _____

Month	Contribution	Earnings	Withdrawals
January:	$_____	$_____	$_____
February:	_____	_____	_____
March:	_____	_____	_____
April:	_____	_____	_____
May:	_____	_____	_____
June:	_____	_____	_____
July:	_____	_____	_____
August:	_____	_____	_____
September:	_____	_____	_____
October:	_____	_____	_____
November:	_____	_____	_____
December:	_____	_____	_____
Total:	$_____	$_____	$_____

PERSONAL FINANCIAL STATEMENT

Name:_____ Date: _____

Assets:

Cash	$_____
Checking Account(s)	$_____
Savings Account(s)	$_____
Other Savings (CDs, etc.)	$_____
House (market value)	$_____
Other Real Estate (market value)	$_____
Household Furnishings (market value)	$_____
Automobile(s) (blue book value)	$_____
Life Insurance (cash value)	$_____
Stocks, Bonds (current value)	$_____
Retirement Plans/Profit Sharing	$_____
Other Assets	$_____
Total Assets:	**$_____**

Debts:

Mortgages (balance due)	$_____
Installment Loans (balance due)	$_____
Other Loans (balance due)	$_____
Credit Cards (balance due)	$_____
Charge Accounts (amount owed)	$_____
Insurance Premiums Due	$_____
Taxes Owed to Date	$_____
Total Debts:	**$_____**
Net Worth (Total Assets minus Total Debts):	**$_____**

FORM P502

PHILANTHROPIC DONATIONS

Contributor: _____

Donation Period: _____ to _____

Recipient	Date	Contribution	Dollar Amount	Value of Goods
_____	_____	_____	$ _____	$ _____
_____	_____	_____	$ _____	$ _____
_____	_____	_____	$ _____	$ _____
_____	_____	_____	$ _____	$ _____
_____	_____	_____	$ _____	$ _____
_____	_____	_____	$ _____	$ _____
_____	_____	_____	$ _____	$ _____
_____	_____	_____	$ _____	$ _____
_____	_____	_____	$ _____	$ _____
_____	_____	_____	$ _____	$ _____
_____	_____	_____	$ _____	$ _____
_____	_____	_____	$ _____	$ _____
_____	_____	_____	$ _____	$ _____
_____	_____	_____	$ _____	$ _____
_____	_____	_____	$ _____	$ _____
_____	_____	_____	$ _____	$ _____
_____	_____	_____	$ _____	$ _____
_____	_____	_____	$ _____	$ _____
_____	_____	_____	$ _____	$ _____
_____	_____	_____	$ _____	$ _____
_____	_____	_____	$ _____	$ _____
_____	_____	_____	$ _____	$ _____

Total: $ _____ $ _____

PRECIOUS METAL RECORD

Name: _____

Purchase Date	Metal	Purchased From	Purchase Price	Current Value
_____	_____	_____	$_____	$_____
_____	_____	_____	$_____	$_____
_____	_____	_____	$_____	$_____
_____	_____	_____	$_____	$_____
_____	_____	_____	$_____	$_____
_____	_____	_____	$_____	$_____
_____	_____	_____	$_____	$_____
_____	_____	_____	$_____	$_____
_____	_____	_____	$_____	$_____
_____	_____	_____	$_____	$_____
_____	_____	_____	$_____	$_____
_____	_____	_____	$_____	$_____
_____	_____	_____	$_____	$_____
_____	_____	_____	$_____	$_____
_____	_____	_____	$_____	$_____
_____	_____	_____	$_____	$_____
_____	_____	_____	$_____	$_____
_____	_____	_____	$_____	$_____
_____	_____	_____	$_____	$_____
_____	_____	_____	$_____	$_____
_____	_____	_____	$_____	$_____
_____	_____	_____	$_____	$_____

FORM P504

PROPERTY AND LIABILITY INSURANCE COVERAGE

Name of Insured: _____

Property Covered: _____

Property Description: _____

_____

Address: _____

_____

Insurance Provider: _____ Policy #: _____

Coverage

Dwelling Amount: $_____ Other Buildings: $ _____

Personal Property: $ _____ Living Expense: $_____

Personal Liability: $ _____ Public Liability: $_____

Deductibles: $ _____ Premium: $ _____

Premium Due: _____ Expires: _____

Additional Coverages: _____

_____

_____

Insurance Agent: _____ Phone: _____

Address: _____

Policyholder Service or Claims Phone: _____

Insurance Policy Location: _____

Property Inventory Location: _____

Additional Information: _____

_____

_____

_____

RECORD OF INCOME

Name: _____

Quarter: _____ Year: _____

Week Ending	Hours Reg.	O.T.	Deductions Fed. W.H.	St. W.H.	FICA	Net Pay
_____	_____	_____	$ _____	$ _____	$ _____	$ _____
_____	_____	_____	$ _____	$ _____	$ _____	$ _____
_____	_____	_____	$ _____	$ _____	$ _____	$ _____
_____	_____	_____	$ _____	$ _____	$ _____	$ _____
_____	_____	_____	$ _____	$ _____	$ _____	$ _____
_____	_____	_____	$ _____	$ _____	$ _____	$ _____
_____	_____	_____	$ _____	$ _____	$ _____	$ _____
_____	_____	_____	$ _____	$ _____	$ _____	$ _____
_____	_____	_____	$ _____	$ _____	$ _____	$ _____
_____	_____	_____	$ _____	$ _____	$ _____	$ _____
_____	_____	_____	$ _____	$ _____	$ _____	$ _____
_____	_____	_____	$ _____	$ _____	$ _____	$ _____
_____	_____	_____	$ _____	$ _____	$ _____	$ _____
_____	_____	_____	$ _____	$ _____	$ _____	$ _____
_____	_____	_____	$ _____	$ _____	$ _____	$ _____
_____	_____	_____	$ _____	$ _____	$ _____	$ _____
_____	_____	_____	$ _____	$ _____	$ _____	$ _____
_____	_____	_____	$ _____	$ _____	$ _____	$ _____
Quarter Total:	_____	_____	$ _____	$ _____	$ _____	$ _____

FORM R501

RETIREMENT EXPENSES

Name:_____ Year:_____

	Yourself	Spouse	Total
Living Expenses			
Rent/Mortgage Payment	$_____	$_____	$_____
Food	_____	_____	_____
Clothing	_____	_____	_____
Utilities	_____	_____	_____
Home Maint./Improvements	_____	_____	_____
Auto/Transportation	_____	_____	_____
Membership Fees	_____	_____	_____
Entertainment/Rec.	_____	_____	_____
Furniture/Durable Goods	_____	_____	_____
Medical Expenses	_____	_____	_____
Charge Card Payments	_____	_____	_____
Travel	_____	_____	_____
Insurance: Auto	_____	_____	_____
Life	_____	_____	_____
Health	_____	_____	_____
Legal Fees	_____	_____	_____
Loan Payments	_____	_____	_____
Other:_____	_____	_____	_____
Total Living Expenses	$_____	$_____	$_____

	Yourself	Spouse	Total
Income			
Social Security	$_____	$_____	$_____
Pension Plan	_____	_____	_____
Profit Sharing	_____	_____	_____
IRA/Keogh	_____	_____	_____
Private Annuity	_____	_____	_____
Interest on Savings	_____	_____	_____
Interest on Bonds	_____	_____	_____
Stock Dividends	_____	_____	_____
Rental Income	_____	_____	_____
Other:_____	_____	_____	_____
_____	_____	_____	_____
Total Income	$_____	$_____	$_____

	Yourself	Spouse	Total
Taxes			
Federal Income Tax	$_____	$_____	$_____
State/City Income Tax	_____	_____	_____
Property Taxes	_____	_____	_____
Total Taxes	$_____	$_____	$_____

RETURNS ON INVESTMENTS

Name: _____

Time Period Covered: _____

Date Return Received	Total Amount Invested	Investment Source	Return on Investment
_____	$ _____	_____	$ _____
_____	$ _____	_____	$ _____
_____	$ _____	_____	$ _____
_____	$ _____	_____	$ _____
_____	$ _____	_____	$ _____
_____	$ _____	_____	$ _____
_____	$ _____	_____	$ _____
_____	$ _____	_____	$ _____
_____	$ _____	_____	$ _____
_____	$ _____	_____	$ _____
_____	$ _____	_____	$ _____
_____	$ _____	_____	$ _____
_____	$ _____	_____	$ _____
_____	$ _____	_____	$ _____
_____	$ _____	_____	$ _____
_____	$ _____	_____	$ _____
_____	$ _____	_____	$ _____
_____	$ _____	_____	$ _____
_____	$ _____	_____	$ _____
_____	$ _____	_____	$ _____

FORM R504

SALE OF BONDS

Seller's Name: _____

Date of Sale: _____ Purchaser: _____

Bond:_____ Type of Bond: _____

Coupon Rate: _____

Face Value: $ _____ Selling Price: $ _____

Date of Sale: _____ Purchaser: _____

Bond:_____ Type of Bond: _____

Coupon Rate: _____

Face Value: $ _____ Selling Price: $ _____

Date of Sale: _____ Purchaser: _____

Bond:_____ Type of Bond: _____

Coupon Rate: _____

Face Value: $ _____ Selling Price: $ _____

Date of Sale: _____ Purchaser: _____

Bond:_____ Type of Bond: _____

Coupon Rate: _____

Face Value: $ _____ Selling Price: $ _____

Date of Sale: _____ Purchaser: _____

Bond:_____ Type of Bond: _____

Coupon Rate: _____

Face Value: $ _____ Selling Price: $ _____

SAVINGS BONDS COLLECTION

Name: _____

Description	Bond #	Issue Date	Issue Price	Exp. Date
_____	_____	_____	$ _____	_____
_____	_____	_____	$ _____	_____
_____	_____	_____	$ _____	_____
_____	_____	_____	$ _____	_____
_____	_____	_____	$ _____	_____
_____	_____	_____	$ _____	_____
_____	_____	_____	$ _____	_____
_____	_____	_____	$ _____	_____
_____	_____	_____	$ _____	_____
_____	_____	_____	$ _____	_____
_____	_____	_____	$ _____	_____
_____	_____	_____	$ _____	_____
_____	_____	_____	$ _____	_____
_____	_____	_____	$ _____	_____
_____	_____	_____	$ _____	_____
_____	_____	_____	$ _____	_____
_____	_____	_____	$ _____	_____
_____	_____	_____	$ _____	_____
_____	_____	_____	$ _____	_____
_____	_____	_____	$ _____	_____
_____	_____	_____	$ _____	_____
_____	_____	_____	$ _____	_____
_____	_____	_____	$ _____	_____
_____	_____	_____	$ _____	_____

FORM S502

SAVINGS/CHECKING ACCOUNT RECORD

Account Holder: _____ Date: _____

Savings Account #: _____ Date Opened: _____

Bank: _____ Branch: _____

Branch Address: _____

_____ Phone: _____

Savings Account Balance: $ _____

Minimum Amount Allowed: $ _____

Applicable Charges: $ _____

Interest Rate: _____

Authorized Signatures: _____

Additional Terms: _____

Account Holder: _____ Date: _____

Checking Account #: _____ Date Opened: _____

Bank: _____ Branch: _____

Branch Address: _____

_____ Phone: _____

Checking Account Balance: $ _____

Monthly Charges: $ _____ with Minimum Amount of: $ _____

Per Check Charges: $_____ ATM Charge: $_____ Overdraft Charge: $ _____

Interest Rate: _____

Authorized Signatures: _____

Additional Terms: _____

SOCIAL SECURITY REGISTRY

Name:_____ Social Security #:_____

Date Benefits Begin:_____

Date	Amount Contributed	Comments
_____	$ _____	_____
_____	$ _____	_____
_____	$ _____	_____
_____	$ _____	_____
_____	$ _____	_____
_____	$ _____	_____
_____	$ _____	_____
_____	$ _____	_____
_____	$ _____	_____
_____	$ _____	_____
_____	$ _____	_____
_____	$ _____	_____
_____	$ _____	_____
_____	$ _____	_____
_____	$ _____	_____
_____	$ _____	_____
_____	$ _____	_____
_____	$ _____	_____
_____	$ _____	_____
_____	$ _____	_____
_____	$ _____	_____
_____	$ _____	_____

FORM S504

STOCK PRICE FLUCTUATIONS

Name of Stockholder:_____

Stock	Purchase Price/Price	Current Date	Current Price/Share	Gain Loss (+/-)
_____	$_____	_____	$_____	$_____
_____	$_____	_____	$_____	$_____
_____	$_____	_____	$_____	$_____
_____	$_____	_____	$_____	$_____
_____	$_____	_____	$_____	$_____
_____	$_____	_____	$_____	$_____
_____	$_____	_____	$_____	$_____
_____	$_____	_____	$_____	$_____
_____	$_____	_____	$_____	$_____
_____	$_____	_____	$_____	$_____
_____	$_____	_____	$_____	$_____
_____	$_____	_____	$_____	$_____
_____	$_____	_____	$_____	$_____
_____	$_____	_____	$_____	$_____
_____	$_____	_____	$_____	$_____
_____	$_____	_____	$_____	$_____
_____	$_____	_____	$_____	$_____
_____	$_____	_____	$_____	$_____
_____	$_____	_____	$_____	$_____
_____	$_____	_____	$_____	$_____
_____	$_____	_____	$_____	$_____

STOCK PURCHASES

Name of Purchaser:_____

Date Bought	Stock	# of Shares	Price/ Share	Price Paid	Broker
_____	_____	_____	$_____	$_____	_____
_____	_____	_____	$_____	$_____	_____
_____	_____	_____	$_____	$_____	_____
_____	_____	_____	$_____	$_____	_____
_____	_____	_____	$_____	$_____	_____
_____	_____	_____	$_____	$_____	_____
_____	_____	_____	$_____	$_____	_____
_____	_____	_____	$_____	$_____	_____
_____	_____	_____	$_____	$_____	_____
_____	_____	_____	$_____	$_____	_____
_____	_____	_____	$_____	$_____	_____
_____	_____	_____	$_____	$_____	_____
_____	_____	_____	$_____	$_____	_____
_____	_____	_____	$_____	$_____	_____
_____	_____	_____	$_____	$_____	_____
_____	_____	_____	$_____	$_____	_____
_____	_____	_____	$_____	$_____	_____
_____	_____	_____	$_____	$_____	_____
_____	_____	_____	$_____	$_____	_____
_____	_____	_____	$_____	$_____	_____
_____	_____	_____	$_____	$_____	_____

Total: $_____

FORM S506

STOCK SALES

Name of Seller: _____

Date Sold	Stock	# of Shares	Price/ Share	Price Sold	Broker
_____	_____	_____	$ _____	$ _____	_____
_____	_____	_____	$ _____	$ _____	_____
_____	_____	_____	$ _____	$ _____	_____
_____	_____	_____	$ _____	$ _____	_____
_____	_____	_____	$ _____	$ _____	_____
_____	_____	_____	$ _____	$ _____	_____
_____	_____	_____	$ _____	$ _____	_____
_____	_____	_____	$ _____	$ _____	_____
_____	_____	_____	$ _____	$ _____	_____
_____	_____	_____	$ _____	$ _____	_____
_____	_____	_____	$ _____	$ _____	_____
_____	_____	_____	$ _____	$ _____	_____
_____	_____	_____	$ _____	$ _____	_____
_____	_____	_____	$ _____	$ _____	_____
_____	_____	_____	$ _____	$ _____	_____
_____	_____	_____	$ _____	$ _____	_____
_____	_____	_____	$ _____	$ _____	_____
_____	_____	_____	$ _____	$ _____	_____
_____	_____	_____	$ _____	$ _____	_____
_____	_____	_____	$ _____	$ _____	_____
_____	_____	_____	$ _____	$ _____	_____
_____	_____	_____	$ _____	$ _____	_____

Total: $ _____

TALLY OF DAY-BY-DAY CLOSING BALANCES

Name: _____

	Security	Security	Security	Security
	_____	_____	_____	_____
Day: _____	C_____	C_____	C_____	C_____
	A_____	A_____	A_____	A_____
Day: _____	C_____	C_____	C_____	C_____
	A_____	A_____	A_____	A_____
Day: _____	C_____	C_____	C_____	C_____
	A_____	A_____	A_____	A_____
Day: _____	C_____	C_____	C_____	C_____
	A_____	A_____	A_____	A_____
Day: _____	C_____	C_____	C_____	C_____
	A_____	A_____	A_____	A_____
Day: _____	C_____	C_____	C_____	C_____
	A_____	A_____	A_____	A_____
Day: _____	C_____	C_____	C_____	C_____
	A_____	A_____	A_____	A_____
Day: _____	C_____	C_____	C_____	C_____
	A_____	A_____	A_____	A_____
Day: _____	C_____	C_____	C_____	C_____
	A_____	A_____	A_____	A_____
Day: _____	C_____	C_____	C_____	C_____
	A_____	A_____	A_____	A_____

C = Closing   A = Accounts Value

FORM T501

TAX RECORD FINDER

Name: _____

Current Year:_____

Tax Preparation Service Used: _____

Address: _____

Contact: _____ Phone:_____

Amount Expected to Owe/Receive: $_____

Location of Income Documentation: _____

_____

Location of Expense Documentation: _____

_____

Additional Information:_____

_____

Previous Year: _____

Tax Preparation Service Used: _____

Address: _____

Contact: _____ Phone:_____

Amount Owed/Received: $ _____

Location of Income Documentation: _____

_____

Location of Expense Documentation: _____

_____

Additional Information:_____

_____

UNIT INVESTMENT TRUSTS

Name: _____

Name of Trust	Date Purchased	Units Purchased	Purchase Price	Interest Rate	Date Sold	Sale Price
_____	_____	_____	$_____	_____	_____	$_____
_____	_____	_____	$_____	_____	_____	$_____
_____	_____	_____	$_____	_____	_____	$_____
_____	_____	_____	$_____	_____	_____	$_____
_____	_____	_____	$_____	_____	_____	$_____
_____	_____	_____	$_____	_____	_____	$_____
_____	_____	_____	$_____	_____	_____	$_____
_____	_____	_____	$_____	_____	_____	$_____
_____	_____	_____	$_____	_____	_____	$_____
_____	_____	_____	$_____	_____	_____	$_____
_____	_____	_____	$_____	_____	_____	$_____
_____	_____	_____	$_____	_____	_____	$_____
_____	_____	_____	$_____	_____	_____	$_____
_____	_____	_____	$_____	_____	_____	$_____
_____	_____	_____	$_____	_____	_____	$_____
_____	_____	_____	$_____	_____	_____	$_____
_____	_____	_____	$_____	_____	_____	$_____
_____	_____	_____	$_____	_____	_____	$_____
_____	_____	_____	$_____	_____	_____	$_____
_____	_____	_____	$_____	_____	_____	$_____
_____	_____	_____	$_____	_____	_____	$_____
_____	_____	_____	$_____	_____	_____	$_____
_____	_____	_____	$_____	_____	_____	$_____

FORM U501

U.S. SAVINGS/TREASURY BONDS REGISTRY

Name: _____

Type of Bond	Series #	Amount	Purchase Date	Maturity Date
_____	_____	$ _____	_____	_____
_____	_____	$ _____	_____	_____
_____	_____	$ _____	_____	_____
_____	_____	$ _____	_____	_____
_____	_____	$ _____	_____	_____
_____	_____	$ _____	_____	_____
_____	_____	$ _____	_____	_____
_____	_____	$ _____	_____	_____
_____	_____	$ _____	_____	_____
_____	_____	$ _____	_____	_____
_____	_____	$ _____	_____	_____
_____	_____	$ _____	_____	_____
_____	_____	$ _____	_____	_____
_____	_____	$ _____	_____	_____
_____	_____	$ _____	_____	_____
_____	_____	$ _____	_____	_____
_____	_____	$ _____	_____	_____
_____	_____	$ _____	_____	_____
_____	_____	$ _____	_____	_____
_____	_____	$ _____	_____	_____
_____	_____	$ _____	_____	_____
_____	_____	$ _____	_____	_____
_____	_____	$ _____	_____	_____
_____	_____	$ _____	_____	_____

WILLS AND TRUSTS

Wills

Name:_____ Date Signed:_____

Attorney: _____ Phone: _____

Attorney Address:_____

_____

Executor of Estate: _____ Phone: _____

Executor Address: _____

_____

Location of Original Will: _____

Location of Copies: _____

Codicils (if any): _____

Additional Information:_____

_____

Trusts

Name:_____ Date of Trust:_____

Trustee(s): _____ Phone:_____

Address: _____

_____

Location of Trust Documents:_____

_____

Location of Copies:_____

Amendments (if any): _____

_____

Additional Information:_____

_____

 FORM W501

ZERO COUPON BONDS REGISTRY

Name: _____

Type of Bond	Date Purchased	Purchase Price	Interest Rate	Date of Maturity
_____	_____	$_____	_____	_____
_____	_____	$_____	_____	_____
_____	_____	$_____	_____	_____
_____	_____	$_____	_____	_____
_____	_____	$_____	_____	_____
_____	_____	$_____	_____	_____
_____	_____	$_____	_____	_____
_____	_____	$_____	_____	_____
_____	_____	$_____	_____	_____
_____	_____	$_____	_____	_____
_____	_____	$_____	_____	_____
_____	_____	$_____	_____	_____
_____	_____	$_____	_____	_____
_____	_____	$_____	_____	_____
_____	_____	$_____	_____	_____
_____	_____	$_____	_____	_____
_____	_____	$_____	_____	_____
_____	_____	$_____	_____	_____
_____	_____	$_____	_____	_____
_____	_____	$_____	_____	_____
_____	_____	$_____	_____	_____
_____	_____	$_____	_____	_____
_____	_____	$_____	_____	_____

Section 6
Purchase and Maintenance Records

Form C601   **Catalog/Mail Order Register** – Organizes information on products ordered through catalogs or by mail

Form E601   **Equipment Service Log** – Provides service record for certain equipment or machinery

Form H601   **Home Improvement Project** – Assembles material and labor costs for planned home remodeling or renovation projects

Form H602   **Homeowner's Vital Data Record** – Lists mortgage deed information

Form H603   **Home Property Assessments** – Provides inventory and value price of household items

Form M601   **Major Purchases Inventory** – Records purchases of major items

Form O601   **Order Information Sheet** – Compiles list of things to order and whom to order from

Form R601   **Record of Subscriptions** – Keeps record of past and current subscriptions

Form V601   **Vehicle Maintenance Schedule** – Provides checklist for routine maintenance services

Form V602   **Vehicle Service Log** – Provides list of vehicle repairs made

Form W601   **Warranties on Purchased Products** – Logs warranty and expiration dates on products purchased

CATALOG/MAIL ORDER REGISTER

Name: _____

Item Ordered: _____ Number:_____

Quantity: _____ Price Each: $ _____ Total: $ _____

Ordered From: _____ Phone: _____

Address: _____

Date Ordered: _____ Date Received: _____ Payment Method:_____

Item Ordered: _____ Number:_____

Quantity: _____ Price Each: $ _____ Total: $ _____

Ordered From: _____ Phone: _____

Address: _____

Date Ordered: _____ Date Received: _____ Payment Method:_____

Item Ordered: _____ Number:_____

Quantity: _____ Price Each: $ _____ Total: $ _____

Ordered From: _____ Phone: _____

Address: _____

Date Ordered: _____ Date Received: _____ Payment Method:_____

Item Ordered: _____ Number:_____

Quantity: _____ Price Each: $ _____ Total: $ _____

Ordered From: _____ Phone: _____

Address: _____

Date Ordered: _____ Date Received: _____ Payment Method:_____

EQUIPMENT SERVICE LOG

Equipment/Machinery: _____

Name of Manufacturer: _____

Model: _____ Purchase Date: _____

Serial #: _____ Year: _____ Price: $_____

Purchased From: _____

Address: _____

Phone: _____ Warranty Expires: _____

Service Contract With: _____

Address: _____

Service Record:

Date   Service

_____   _____

_____   _____

_____   _____

_____   _____

_____   _____

_____   _____

_____   _____

_____   _____

_____   _____

_____   _____

_____   _____

_____   _____

FORM E601

HOME IMPROVEMENT PROJECT

Description of Project: _____

_____

_____

Location of Property: _____

Project Starting Date: _____ Est. Date of Completion: _____

Budgeted Amount: $_____ Actual Cost: $_____

Contracting Firm/Contractor(s): _____

_____

_____

_____

Materials Used	Cost
_____	$_____
_____	$_____
_____	$_____
_____	$_____
_____	$_____

Labor	Cost
_____	$_____
_____	$_____
_____	$_____
_____	$_____
_____	$_____

Other Details:_____

_____

Location of Receipts/Records: _____

_____

HOMEOWNER'S VITAL DATA RECORD

Title Owner(s): _____

_____

Property Location: _____

Property Description: _____

_____

_____

_____

Date Purchased: _____ Purchase Price: $ _____

Name of Seller(s): _____

Mortgage Holder: _____

Address: _____

Phone: _____

Holder of Contract for Deed: _____

Contract Amount: $ _____ Interest Rate: _____ Due: _____

Assessed Value: $ _____ Date: _____

Location of Deed: _____

Deed Register Number: _____

Location of Property Tax Records: _____

Terms: _____

_____

_____

Other Information: _____

_____

_____

_____

FORM H602

HOME PROPERTY ASSESSMENTS

Item	Purchase Date	Price Paid	Current Date	Current Value
_____	_____	$ _____	_____	$ _____
_____	_____	$ _____	_____	$ _____
_____	_____	$ _____	_____	$ _____
_____	_____	$ _____	_____	$ _____
_____	_____	$ _____	_____	$ _____
_____	_____	$ _____	_____	$ _____
_____	_____	$ _____	_____	$ _____
_____	_____	$ _____	_____	$ _____
_____	_____	$ _____	_____	$ _____
_____	_____	$ _____	_____	$ _____
_____	_____	$ _____	_____	$ _____
_____	_____	$ _____	_____	$ _____
_____	_____	$ _____	_____	$ _____
_____	_____	$ _____	_____	$ _____
_____	_____	$ _____	_____	$ _____
_____	_____	$ _____	_____	$ _____
_____	_____	$ _____	_____	$ _____
_____	_____	$ _____	_____	$ _____
_____	_____	$ _____	_____	$ _____
_____	_____	$ _____	_____	$ _____
_____	_____	$ _____	_____	$ _____
_____	_____	$ _____	_____	$ _____
_____	_____	$ _____	_____	$ _____
_____	_____	$ _____	_____	$ _____
_____	_____	$ _____	_____	$ _____
	_____	$ _____		$ _____

MAJOR PURCHASES INVENTORY

Name: _____

Item Purchased: _____

Date Purchased: _____ Purchase Location: _____

Model Number: _____ Serial Number: _____

Cost: _____ Payment Method: _____

Terms of Guarantee/Warranty: _____

For Service Call: _____ Phone: _____

Additional Information: _____

_____

Name: _____

Item Purchased: _____

Date Purchased: _____ Purchase Location: _____

Model Number: _____ Serial Number: _____

Cost: _____ Payment Method: _____

Terms of Guarantee/Warranty: _____

For Service Call: _____ Phone: _____

Additional Information: _____

_____

Name: _____

Item Purchased: _____

Date Purchased: _____ Purchase Location: _____

Model Number: _____ Serial Number: _____

Cost: _____ Payment Method: _____

Terms of Guarantee/Warranty: _____

For Service Call: _____ Phone: _____

Additional Information: _____

_____

ORDER INFORMATION SHEET

Name: _____

Item: _____ Order Date: _____

Ordered From: _____

Address: _____

Phone: _____

Price: $ _____ Ship Via: _____ Date Received: _____

Name: _____

Item: _____ Order Date: _____

Ordered From: _____

Address: _____

Phone: _____

Price: $ _____ Ship Via: _____ Date Received: _____

Name: _____

Item: _____ Order Date: _____

Ordered From: _____

Address: _____

Phone: _____

Price: $ _____ Ship Via: _____ Date Received: _____

Name: _____

Item: _____ Order Date: _____

Ordered From: _____

Address: _____

Phone: _____

Price: $ _____ Ship Via: _____ Date Received: _____

RECORD OF SUBSCRIPTIONS

Name: _____

Name of Publication: _____

Address: _____

Phone: _____

Date Subscribed: _____ Cost: $_____ Renewal Date: _____

Length of Subscription:_____ Number of Issues:_____

Name: _____

Name of Publication: _____

Address: _____

Phone: _____

Date Subscribed: _____ Cost: $_____ Renewal Date: _____

Length of Subscription:_____ Number of Issues:_____

Name: _____

Name of Publication: _____

Address: _____

Phone: _____

Date Subscribed: _____ Cost: $_____ Renewal Date: _____

Length of Subscription:_____ Number of Issues:_____

Name: _____

Name of Publication: _____

Address: _____

Phone: _____

Date Subscribed: _____ Cost: $_____ Renewal Date: _____

Length of Subscription:_____ Number of Issues:_____

FORM R601

VEHICLE MAINTENANCE SCHEDULE

Vehicle: _____

Services:	Date	Vehicle Mileage	Cost	Service Station	Next Service
Tune-up	_____	_____	$ _____	_____	_____
Tire Change	_____	_____	$ _____	_____	_____
Wheel Alignment	_____	_____	$ _____	_____	_____
Wheel Balance	_____	_____	$ _____	_____	_____
Oil Change	_____	_____	$ _____	_____	_____
Filter Change	_____	_____	$ _____	_____	_____
Battery	_____	_____	$ _____	_____	_____
Other ( )	_____	_____	$ _____	_____	_____
Additional Information:	_____	_____	$ _____	_____	_____

Vehicle: _____

Services:	Date	Vehicle Mileage	Cost	Service Station	Next Service
Tune-up	_____	_____	$ _____	_____	_____
Tire Change	_____	_____	$ _____	_____	_____
Wheel Alignment	_____	_____	$ _____	_____	_____
Wheel Balance	_____	_____	$ _____	_____	_____
Oil Change	_____	_____	$ _____	_____	_____
Filter Change	_____	_____	$ _____	_____	_____
Battery	_____	_____	$ _____	_____	_____
Other ( )	_____	_____	$ _____	_____	_____
Additional Information:	_____	_____	$ _____	_____	_____

VEHICLE SERVICE LOG

Vehicle: _____

Owner: _____

Date	Type of Repair	Cost of Repair	Mechanic/Garage
_____	_____	$ _____	_____
_____	_____	$ _____	_____
_____	_____	$ _____	_____
_____	_____	$ _____	_____
_____	_____	$ _____	_____
_____	_____	$ _____	_____
_____	_____	$ _____	_____
_____	_____	$ _____	_____
_____	_____	$ _____	_____
_____	_____	$ _____	_____
_____	_____	$ _____	_____
_____	_____	$ _____	_____
_____	_____	$ _____	_____
_____	_____	$ _____	_____
_____	_____	$ _____	_____
_____	_____	$ _____	_____
_____	_____	$ _____	_____
_____	_____	$ _____	_____
_____	_____	$ _____	_____
_____	_____	$ _____	_____

Total: $ _____

FORM V602

WARRANTIES ON PURCHASED PRODUCTS

Name: _____

Product: _____

Purchase Location: _____

Date Purchased: _____ Cost: $ _____

Warranty Terms: _____

_____

Warranty Card/Sales Receipt Location: _____

Warranty Exp. Date: _____ For Service Call: _____

Other Information: _____

Product: _____

Purchase Location: _____

Date Purchased: _____ Cost: $ _____

Warranty Terms: _____

_____

Warranty Card/Sales Receipt Location: _____

Warranty Exp. Date: _____ For Service Call: _____

Other Information: _____

Product: _____

Purchase Location: _____

Date Purchased: _____ Cost: $ _____

Warranty Terms: _____

_____

Warranty Card/Sales Receipt Location: _____

Warranty Exp. Date: _____ For Service Call: _____

Other Information: _____

Section 7
Important Names, Dates and Facts

Form C701   **Club/Organization Member List** – Provides roster for organization members

Form C702   **Commonly Called Numbers** – Lists frequently called phone numbers

Form C703   **Correspondence Reminder List** – Reminder of whom to contact and why

Form D701   **Death Notification Listing** – Lists people to contact following the death of a loved one

Form D702   **Directory of Professional/Consultation Services** – Reference guide to professional services

Form E701   **Emergency Phone Number Listing** – Lists whom to call in case of an emergency

Form I701   **Important Birthdays** – Lists dates and gift ideas for birthdays to remember

Form I702   **Important Occasions to Remember** – Lists dates and gift ideas for important anniversaries and other occasions to remember

Form I703   **Important Phone Numbers** – A personal directory of services used

Form O701   **Officers and Directors** – Roster of an organization's officers and directors

Form O702   **Organization and Club Affiliations** – Lists associations with various organizations and their vital data

Form R701   **References** – Gathers references often used for job, loan and other applications

CLUB/ORGANIZATION MEMBER LIST

Organization: _____ Date: _____

Member Name: _____ Phone: _____

Address: _____

Member Name: _____ Phone: _____

Address: _____

Member Name: _____ Phone: _____

Address: _____

Member Name: _____ Phone: _____

Address: _____

Member Name: _____ Phone: _____

Address: _____

Member Name: _____ Phone: _____

Address: _____

Member Name: _____ Phone: _____

Address: _____

Member Name: _____ Phone: _____

Address: _____

COMMONLY CALLED NUMBERS

Name   Phone

_____   _____

_____   _____

_____   _____

_____   _____

_____   _____

_____   _____

_____   _____

_____   _____

_____   _____

_____   _____

_____   _____

_____   _____

_____   _____

_____   _____

_____   _____

_____   _____

_____   _____

_____   _____

_____   _____

_____   _____

FORM C702

CORRESPONDENCE REMINDER LIST

Name: _____

Correspond with: _____ by: _____

    Address: _____

    _____ Phone: _____

    Regarding: _____

Correspond with: _____ by: _____

    Address: _____

    _____ Phone: _____

    Regarding: _____

Correspond with: _____ by: _____

    Address: _____

    _____ Phone: _____

    Regarding: _____

Correspond with: _____ by: _____

    Address: _____

    _____ Phone: _____

    Regarding: _____

Correspond with: _____ by: _____

    Address: _____

    _____ Phone: _____

    Regarding: _____

DEATH NOTIFICATION LISTING

Name of Deceased: _____

Accountant: _____ Phone: _____

    Address: _____

Attorney: _____ Phone: _____

    Address: _____

Banker: _____ Phone: _____

    Address: _____

Clergyman/Rabbi: _____ Phone: _____

    Address: _____

(Will) Executor: _____ Phone: _____

    Address: _____

(Alternate) Executor: _____ Phone: _____

    Address: _____

Funeral Director: _____ Phone: _____

    Address: _____

Guardian: _____ Phone: _____

    Address: _____

(Contingent) Guardian: _____ Phone: _____

    Address: _____

Insurance Agent: _____ Phone: _____

    Address: _____

Insurance Underwriter: _____ Phone: _____

    Address: _____

FORM D701

DIRECTORY OF PROFESSIONAL/CONSULTATION SERVICES

Name of Consultant/Service: _____

Company/Organization: _____

Address: _____

Phone: _____

Rate per Hour: _____ Availability: _____

Name of Consultant/Service: _____

Company/Organization: _____

Address: _____

Phone: _____

Rate per Hour: _____ Availability: _____

Name of Consultant/Service: _____

Company/Organization: _____

Address: _____

Phone: _____

Rate per Hour: _____ Availability: _____

Name of Consultant/Service: _____

Company/Organization: _____

Address: _____

Phone: _____

Rate per Hour: _____ Availability: _____

Name of Consultant/Service: _____

Company/Organization: _____

Address: _____

Phone: _____

Rate per Hour: _____ Availability: _____

EMERGENCY PHONE NUMBER LISTING

For: _____

Address: _____

Phone

Fire Department _____

Police Department _____

Hospital _____

Physician _____

Poison Control _____

Ambulance _____

Pharmacy _____

Security Alarm Company _____

Animal Control _____

Work Phone Numbers _____

_____

_____

Neighbors

_____   _____

_____   _____

_____   _____

Relatives

_____   _____

_____   _____

_____   _____

FORM E701

IMPORTANT BIRTHDAYS

Year:_____

Celebrant	Birthdate	Age	Gift Ideas

IMPORTANT OCCASIONS TO REMEMBER

Month: _____ Year: _____

Name	Occasion	Event Date	Event Time
_____	_____	_____	_____
_____	_____	_____	_____
_____	_____	_____	_____
_____	_____	_____	_____
_____	_____	_____	_____
_____	_____	_____	_____
_____	_____	_____	_____
_____	_____	_____	_____
_____	_____	_____	_____
_____	_____	_____	_____
_____	_____	_____	_____
_____	_____	_____	_____
_____	_____	_____	_____
_____	_____	_____	_____
_____	_____	_____	_____
_____	_____	_____	_____
_____	_____	_____	_____
_____	_____	_____	_____
_____	_____	_____	_____
_____	_____	_____	_____
_____	_____	_____	_____
_____	_____	_____	_____

FORM I702

IMPORTANT PHONE NUMBERS

Medical Doctor: _____ Phone: _____

    Address: _____

Veterinarian: _____ Phone: _____

    Address: _____

Pediatrician: _____ Phone: _____

    Address: _____

Hairdresser: _____ Phone: _____

    Address: _____

Manicurist: _____ Phone: _____

    Address: _____

Dentist: _____ Phone: _____

    Address: _____

Orthodontist: _____ Phone: _____

    Address: _____

Gynecologist: _____ Phone: _____

    Address: _____

Attorney: _____ Phone: _____

    Address: _____

Accountant: _____ Phone: _____

    Address: _____

Gym: _____ Phone: _____

    Address: _____

Babysitter: _____ Phone: _____

    Address: _____

Other Important Numbers: _____

_____

OFFICERS AND DIRECTORS

Organization: _____

Name	Title	Phone
_____	_____	_____
_____	_____	_____
_____	_____	_____
_____	_____	_____
_____	_____	_____
_____	_____	_____

Organization: _____

Name	Title	Phone
_____	_____	_____
_____	_____	_____
_____	_____	_____
_____	_____	_____
_____	_____	_____
_____	_____	_____

Organization: _____

Name	Title	Phone
_____	_____	_____
_____	_____	_____
_____	_____	_____
_____	_____	_____
_____	_____	_____

FORM O701

ORGANIZATION & CLUB AFFILIATIONS

Organization: _____ Phone: _____

Address: _____

Membership Date: _____ Annual Dues:_____ Expiration Date: _____

President:_____ Phone: _____

Organization: _____ Phone: _____

Address: _____

Membership Date: _____ Annual Dues:_____ Expiration Date: _____

President:_____ Phone: _____

Organization: _____ Phone: _____

Address: _____

Membership Date: _____ Annual Dues:_____ Expiration Date: _____

President:_____ Phone: _____

Organization: _____ Phone: _____

Address: _____

Membership Date: _____ Annual Dues:_____ Expiration Date: _____

President:_____ Phone: _____

Organization: _____ Phone: _____

Address: _____

Membership Date: _____ Annual Dues:_____ Expiration Date: _____

President:_____ Phone: _____

REFERENCES

Name: _____

Reference's Name and Title: _____

_____

    Home Address: _____

    Phone: _____

    Company Name: _____

    Address: _____

    Phone: _____

    Used as a Reference for: _____ Date: _____

                                         _____ Date: _____

                                         _____ Date: _____

Reference's Name and Title: _____

_____

    Home Address: _____

    Phone: _____

    Company Name: _____

    Address: _____

    Phone: _____

    Used as a Reference for: _____ Date: _____

                                         _____ Date: _____

                                         _____ Date: _____

FORM R701

Section 8
Event Planning

Form A801   **Anniversary Party Planning Record** – Assists in planning an anniversary party

Form A802   **Announcement Guest List** – Invitation list for upcoming announcement

Form B801   **Baby Shower Organizer** – Assists in planning a baby shower

Form B802   **Bridal Shower Organizer** – Assists in planning a bridal shower

Form C801   **Christmas Party Planning Record** – Assists in planning a Christmas party

Form F801   **Funeral Planning Guide** – Assists in planning a funeral service

Form G801   **Gift-Giving Record** – Keeps record of gifts given

Form G802   **Guest Invitation Registry** – Guest register for upcoming event

Form H801   **Holiday Gift-Giving Registry** – Listing of holiday gifts given

Form I801   **Invitation Response Form** – Lists RSVPs from invited guests

Form N801   **New Year's Eve Party Planner** – Assists in planning a New Year's Eve party

Form R801   **Religious Events** – Lists planned religious events

Form R802   **Retirement Party Planner** – Assists in planning a retirement party

Form S801   **Special Dinner Party Planner** – Suggestions for planning a special dinner engagement

ANNIVERSARY PARTY PLANNING RECORD

Guests of Honor: _____

Host(s): _____

Party Date:_____ Time: _____

Party Location:_____

Gift Ideas

_____   _____

_____   _____

_____   _____

_____   _____

_____   _____

Refreshment Suggestions

_____   _____

_____   _____

_____   _____

Decoration Ideas

_____   _____

_____   _____

_____   _____

Invitations

Date Sent: _____ # Sent: _____

RSVPs: # of Guests Attending: _____ # Not Attending: _____

Additional Information:_____

_____

_____

ANNOUNCEMENT GUEST LIST

Upcoming Event:_____

Host(s):_____ Announcement Date: _____

Name:_____ Phone: _____

Address: _____

Name:_____ Phone: _____

Address: _____

Name:_____ Phone: _____

Address: _____

Name:_____ Phone: _____

Address: _____

Name:_____ Phone: _____

Address: _____

Name:_____ Phone: _____

Address: _____

Name:_____ Phone: _____

Address: _____

Name:_____ Phone: _____

Address: _____

FORM A802

BABY SHOWER ORGANIZER

Name of New Mother: _____

Host(s): _____

Date of Shower: _____ Time of Shower: _____

Location of Shower: _____

_____

Expected Baby Delivery Date: _____ Sex of Baby: _____

Name of Baby: _____

Gift Ideas

_____   _____

_____   _____

_____   _____

_____   _____

_____   _____

Refreshment Suggestions

_____   _____

_____   _____

_____   _____

Decoration Ideas

_____   _____

_____   _____

_____   _____

Invitations

Date Sent: _____   # Sent: _____

RSVPs: # of Guests Attending: _____ # Not Attending: _____

Additional Information: _____

_____

_____

BRIDAL SHOWER ORGANIZER

Name of Bride-to-Be: _____

Host(s): _____

Date of Shower: _____ Time of Shower: _____

Location of Shower: _____

_____

Gift Ideas

_____   _____

_____   _____

_____   _____

_____   _____

_____   _____

Refreshment Suggestions

_____   _____

_____   _____

Decoration Ideas

_____   _____

_____   _____

_____   _____

Invitations

Date Sent: _____ # Sent: _____

RSVPs: # of Guests Attending: _____ # Not Attending: _____

Additional Information: _____

_____

_____

FORM B802

CHRISTMAS PARTY PLANNING RECORD

Host(s): _____

Party Date: _____ Party Time: _____

Location: _____

Guest List

_____ _____ _____

_____ _____ _____

_____ _____ _____

_____ _____ _____

_____ _____ _____

_____ _____ _____

Refreshment Suggestions

_____ _____

_____ _____

_____ _____

Decoration Ideas

_____ _____

_____ _____

_____ _____

Invitations

Date Sent: _____ # Sent: _____

RSVPs: # of Guests Attending: _____ # Not Attending: _____

Additional Information: _____

_____

_____

FUNERAL PLANNING GUIDE

Name of Deceased: _____

Funeral Home: _____

Address: _____

Funeral Plan: _____

Director: _____ Phone: _____

Type of Service: Religious _____ Military _____ Fraternal _____

Officiator:_____ Phone: _____

Music Selections: _____

Reading Selections: _____

Flowers: _____

Memorials: _____

Pallbearers: _____

Disposition of Remains

Burial: Name of Cemetery: _____

    Location: _____

    Section: _____ Plot #: _____ Block: _____

    Deed Location:_____

    Other Instructions: _____

Cremation: Disposition of Ashes:_____

    Cremation Performed at: _____

    Other Instructions: _____

Coverage of Funeral Expenses

Life Insurance: _____

Burial Insurance: _____ Fraternal Organizations(s): _____

Social Security:_____ Veteran's Administration:_____

Pension Benefit:_____ Union Benefit:_____

GIFT-GIVING RECORD

Name:_____ Date: _____

Gift	Date Given	Occasion	Cost	Recipient
_____	_____	_____	$ _____	_____
_____	_____	_____	$ _____	_____
_____	_____	_____	$ _____	_____
_____	_____	_____	$ _____	_____
_____	_____	_____	$ _____	_____
_____	_____	_____	$ _____	_____
_____	_____	_____	$ _____	_____
_____	_____	_____	$ _____	_____
_____	_____	_____	$ _____	_____
_____	_____	_____	$ _____	_____
_____	_____	_____	$ _____	_____
_____	_____	_____	$ _____	_____
_____	_____	_____	$ _____	_____
_____	_____	_____	$ _____	_____
_____	_____	_____	$ _____	_____
_____	_____	_____	$ _____	_____
_____	_____	_____	$ _____	_____
_____	_____	_____	$ _____	_____
_____	_____	_____	$ _____	_____
_____	_____	_____	$ _____	_____
_____	_____	_____	$ _____	_____
_____	_____	_____	$ _____	_____
_____	_____	_____	$ _____	_____
_____	_____	_____	$ _____	_____
_____	_____	_____	$ _____	_____

GUEST INVITATION REGISTRY

Occasion: _____

Date of Occasion: _____ Time: _____

Location: _____

Guest   Address

_____   _____

_____   _____

_____   _____

_____   _____

_____   _____

_____   _____

_____   _____

_____   _____

_____   _____

_____   _____

_____   _____

_____   _____

_____   _____

_____   _____

_____   _____

_____   _____

_____   _____

_____   _____

_____   _____

FORM G802

HOLIDAY GIFT-GIVING REGISTRY

Name: _____

Holiday: _____ Date: _____

Gift Recipient	Gift	Cost	Date Sent
_____	_____	$ _____	_____
_____	_____	$ _____	_____
_____	_____	$ _____	_____
_____	_____	$ _____	_____
_____	_____	$ _____	_____
_____	_____	$ _____	_____
_____	_____	$ _____	_____
_____	_____	$ _____	_____
_____	_____	$ _____	_____
_____	_____	$ _____	_____
_____	_____	$ _____	_____
_____	_____	$ _____	_____
_____	_____	$ _____	_____
_____	_____	$ _____	_____
_____	_____	$ _____	_____
_____	_____	$ _____	_____
_____	_____	$ _____	_____
_____	_____	$ _____	_____
_____	_____	$ _____	_____
_____	_____	$ _____	_____
_____	_____	$ _____	_____
_____	_____	$ _____	_____
_____	_____	$ _____	_____
_____	_____	$ _____	_____

INVITATION RESPONSE FORM

Event: _____ Date: _____

Guest(s) Invited	Phone	RSVP	RSVP Date
_____	_____	_____	_____
_____	_____	_____	_____
_____	_____	_____	_____
_____	_____	_____	_____
_____	_____	_____	_____
_____	_____	_____	_____
_____	_____	_____	_____
_____	_____	_____	_____
_____	_____	_____	_____
_____	_____	_____	_____
_____	_____	_____	_____
_____	_____	_____	_____
_____	_____	_____	_____
_____	_____	_____	_____
_____	_____	_____	_____
_____	_____	_____	_____
_____	_____	_____	_____
_____	_____	_____	_____
_____	_____	_____	_____
_____	_____	_____	_____
_____	_____	_____	_____
_____	_____	_____	_____

FORM I801

NEW YEAR'S EVE PARTY PLANNER

Host(s): _____

Party Time: _____ Location: _____

Guest List

_____ _____ _____

_____ _____ _____

_____ _____ _____

_____ _____ _____

_____ _____ _____

Refreshment Suggestions

_____ _____

_____ _____

_____ _____

_____ _____

Decoration Ideas

_____ _____

_____ _____

_____ _____

Special Midnight Activities: _____

_____

Invitations

Date Sent: _____ # Sent: _____

RSVPs: # of Guests Attending: _____ # Not Attending: _____

Additional Information: _____

_____

RELIGIOUS EVENTS

Event:_____

Date: _____ Time: _____ Place: _____

Name of Clergyman:_____

In Attendance

_____   _____   _____
_____   _____   _____
_____   _____   _____
_____   _____   _____
_____   _____   _____
_____   _____   _____
_____   _____   _____
_____   _____   _____
_____   _____   _____
_____   _____   _____
_____   _____   _____
_____   _____   _____
_____   _____   _____
_____   _____   _____
_____   _____   _____

Additional Information:_____

_____

FORM R801

RETIREMENT PARTY PLANNER

Host(s): _____

For: _____ Phone: _____

Retiring from:_____

Party Date:_____ Time: _____

Location: _____

Gift Ideas

_____   _____

_____   _____

_____   _____

_____   _____

_____   _____

Refreshment Suggestions

_____   _____

_____   _____

_____   _____

_____   _____

Decoration Ideas

_____   _____

_____   _____

_____   _____

_____   _____

Invitations

Date Sent: _____ # Sent: _____

RSVPs: # of Guests Attending: _____ # Not Attending: _____

Additional Information:_____

_____

_____

SPECIAL DINNER PARTY PLANNER

Host(s): _____

Location: _____

Date: _____ Time: _____

Dinner Party Guest(s)

_____ _____ _____

_____ _____ _____

_____ _____ _____

_____ _____ _____

_____ _____ _____

Dinner Served

Cocktails: _____

Appetizer: _____

Salad: _____

Wine: _____

Entree: _____

Side Dishes: _____

Dessert: _____

Coffee: _____

Liqueurs/Cordials: _____

Music: _____

Flowers: _____

Table Arrangement: _____

Guests' Allergies/Dislikes: _____

_____

Special Diet Options: _____

_____

Section 9
Travel Data

Form L901   **Log of Frequent Flyer Miles** – Tracks miles logged on airline flights

Form N901   **Nautical Log** – Provides boat and cruise information

Form P901   **Passport Listing** – Reference guide to passports issued

Form P902   **Places to Go** – List of domestic and foreign travel ideas

Form P903   **Places Visited** – Catalog of places visited

Form P904   **Plane/Boat Ownership Record** – Vital data on planes and boats owned

Form T901   **Travel Agenda** – Lists hotel and event information for trips taken

Form T902   **Travel Checklist** – List of items to take on upcoming trip

Form T903   **Travel Itinerary** – Details hotel, flight and transportation for upcoming travel

Form V901   **Vacation Log** – Lists comments about trips taken

Form V902   **Visa Record** – Lists all visa information

Form V903   **Visitors' Schedule** – Activity and date planner for visiting guests

LOG OF FREQUENT FLYER MILES

Name: _____ Frequent Flyer # _____

Airline: _____

Date	From	To	Ticket #	Miles	Total Miles
_____	_____	_____	_____	_____	_____
_____	_____	_____	_____	_____	_____
_____	_____	_____	_____	_____	_____
_____	_____	_____	_____	_____	_____
_____	_____	_____	_____	_____	_____
_____	_____	_____	_____	_____	_____
_____	_____	_____	_____	_____	_____
_____	_____	_____	_____	_____	_____
_____	_____	_____	_____	_____	_____
_____	_____	_____	_____	_____	_____
_____	_____	_____	_____	_____	_____
_____	_____	_____	_____	_____	_____
_____	_____	_____	_____	_____	_____
_____	_____	_____	_____	_____	_____
_____	_____	_____	_____	_____	_____
_____	_____	_____	_____	_____	_____
_____	_____	_____	_____	_____	_____
_____	_____	_____	_____	_____	_____
_____	_____	_____	_____	_____	_____
_____	_____	_____	_____	_____	_____

Total: _____

NAUTICAL LOG

Boat/Ship Name: _____

Docked at:_____

Cruise Date:_____ Destination: _____

Time Departed:_____ Time Returned: _____ Fuel: _____

Weather Conditions: _____

Sea Conditions: _____

Passengers

_____   _____

_____   _____

_____   _____

_____   _____

_____   _____

_____   _____

_____   _____

_____   _____

Additional Comments:_____

_____

_____

_____

_____

_____

_____

_____

_____

_____

PASSPORT LISTING

Name: _____

Passport #:_____ Country: _____

Date Issued:_____ Expiration Date: _____

Issuing Authority: _____

Location of Passport: _____

Additional Information: _____

_____

Name: _____

Passport #:_____ Country: _____

Date Issued:_____ Expiration Date: _____

Issuing Authority: _____

Location of Passport: _____

Additional Information: _____

_____

Name: _____

Passport #:_____ Country: _____

Date Issued:_____ Expiration Date: _____

Issuing Authority: _____

Location of Passport: _____

Additional Information: _____

_____

PLACES TO GO

Name:_____ Date: _____

Ideas	Name	Location	Cost:
Museums:	_____	_____	$ _____
Nature Parks:	_____	_____	$ _____
Zoos:	_____	_____	$ _____
Amusement Parks:	_____	_____	$ _____
Famous Buildings:	_____	_____	$ _____
Monuments:	_____	_____	$ _____
Rivers:	_____	_____	$ _____
Lakes:	_____	_____	$ _____
Oceans:	_____	_____	$ _____
Famous Sights:	_____	_____	$ _____
Places to Eat:	_____	_____	$ _____
Concerts:	_____	_____	$ _____
Clubs:	_____	_____	$ _____
Festivals:	_____	_____	$ _____
Arts & Crafts Fairs:	_____	_____	$ _____
Spectator Sports:	_____	_____	$ _____
Participatory Sports:	_____	_____	$ _____
Shopping Centers:	_____	_____	$ _____
Other(s):	_____	_____	$ _____
	_____	_____	$ _____
	_____	_____	$ _____
	_____	_____	$ _____
	_____	_____	$ _____
	_____	_____	$ _____

FORM P902

PLACES VISITED

Name: _____

Place Visited: _____

    Location: _____ Date: from _____ to _____

    Purpose: _____

    People in Party: _____

    _____

    Things Done: _____

    _____

    Sights Seen: _____

    _____

    Additional Comments/Special Moments: _____

    _____

    _____

Place Visited: _____

    Location: _____ Date: from _____ to _____

    Purpose: _____

    People in Party: _____

    _____

    Things Done: _____

    _____

    Sights Seen: _____

    _____

    Additional Comments/Special Moments: _____

    _____

    _____

PLANE/BOAT OWNERSHIP RECORD

Owner's Name: _____ Date Purchased:_____

Purchase Price: _____

Registration #: _____ Registration Date: _____

Purchased from: _____ ID #:_____

Make:_____ Model:_____ Year: _____

Physical Description: _____

_____

_____

_____

Dock/Storage Location: _____

_____

Insured by: _____ Insured Value: $ _____

Liability: $ _____ Contact:_____

Additional Information: _____

_____

_____

_____

_____

_____

_____

_____

_____

_____

_____

_____

FORM P904

TRAVEL AGENDA

Name: _____

Date: _____

Hotel: _____

Location: _____ Phone: _____

Scheduled Appointments/Events: _____

_____

Additional Information: _____

Date: _____

Hotel: _____

Location: _____ Phone: _____

Scheduled Appointments/Events: _____

_____

Additional Information: _____

Date: _____

Hotel: _____

Location: _____ Phone: _____

Scheduled Appointments/Events: _____

_____

Additional Information: _____

Date: _____

Hotel: _____

Location: _____ Phone: _____

Scheduled Appointments/Events: _____

_____

Additional Information: _____

TRAVEL CHECKLIST

Name: _____

Destination: _____

Date of Trip: _____ Length of Trip: _____

Personal Items

_____   _____   _____

_____   _____   _____

_____   _____   _____

Clothing

_____   _____   _____

_____   _____   _____

_____   _____   _____

Business Items

_____   _____   _____

_____   _____   _____

_____   _____   _____

Gifts

_____   _____   _____

_____   _____   _____

_____   _____   _____

Miscellaneous

_____   _____   _____

_____   _____   _____

_____   _____   _____

Form T902

TRAVEL ITINERARY

Name: _____

Destination: _____

Trip Date: _____ to _____

Flight Information

Departure Date: _____ Departure Time: _____

Location: _____

Airline: _____ Flight #: _____ Gate #: _____

Arrival Time: _____ Location: _____

Return Date: _____ Return: _____

Location: _____

Airline: _____ Flight #: _____ Gate #: _____

Arrival Time: _____ Location: _____

Hotel Information

Hotel: _____ Phone #: _____

Address: _____

Date(s) Room Reserved: _____

Bus/Train Information: _____

_____

Rental Car Information: _____

_____

Appointments/Events Scheduled: _____

_____

Important Phone #s: _____

Additional Information: _____

_____

_____

VACATION LOG

Vacation Location: _____ Date: _____

Comments: _____

_____

Vacation Location: _____ Date: _____

Comments: _____

_____

Vacation Location: _____ Date: _____

Comments: _____

_____

Vacation Location: _____ Date: _____

Comments: _____

_____

Vacation Location: _____ Date: _____

Comments: _____

_____

Vacation Location: _____ Date: _____

Comments: _____

_____

Vacation Location: _____ Date: _____

Comments: _____

_____

FORM V901

VISA RECORD

Name: _____

Type of Visa: _____ Visa #: _____

Issued: _____ Country: _____ Expires: _____

Issued by: _____

Visa Location: _____

Additional Information: _____

_____

_____

Name: _____

Type of Visa: _____ Visa #: _____

Issued: _____ Country: _____ Expires: _____

Issued by: _____

Visa Location: _____

Additional Information: _____

_____

_____

Name: _____

Type of Visa: _____ Visa #: _____

Issued: _____ Country: _____ Expires: _____

Issued by: _____

Visa Location: _____

Additional Information: _____

_____

_____

VISITORS' SCHEDULE

Name of Visitor: _____

Dates Visiting: _____

Activities Planned: _____

Additional Information:_____

_____

_____

Name of Visitor: _____

Dates Visiting: _____

Activities Planned: _____

Additional Information:_____

_____

_____

Name of Visitor: _____

Dates Visiting: _____

Activities Planned: _____

Additional Information:_____

_____

_____

Name of Visitor: _____

Dates Visiting: _____

Activities Planned: _____

Additional Information:_____

_____

_____

FORM V903

Section 10
Recreational Activities

Form A110   **Activity Performance Tracking** – Keeps a record of scores on a specific hobby or activity

Form B110   **Book List** – Organizes books owned and read

Form H110   **Hobbies and Interests** – Lists activities related to hobbies or special interests

Form L110   **Library of Audiocassettes** – Itemizes cassettes, records and compact discs owned

Form R110   **Roster of Sporting Results** – Charts the game scores and record of your favorite sports team

Form T110   **Television Viewing Log** – Tracks hours of television watched daily and total hours viewed weekly

Form U110   **Upcoming Entertainment Attractions** – Charts cultural, musical and various other activities to attend

Form V110   **Videocassette Registry** – Library of all videocassettes owned

Form V210   **Videogame Collection** – Itemizes all video game cartridges owned

ACTIVITY PERFORMANCE TRACKING

Name: _____

Activity/Event Performed	Date	Score/ Results	Comments
_____	_____	_____	_____
_____	_____	_____	_____
_____	_____	_____	_____
_____	_____	_____	_____
_____	_____	_____	_____
_____	_____	_____	_____
_____	_____	_____	_____
_____	_____	_____	_____
_____	_____	_____	_____
_____	_____	_____	_____
_____	_____	_____	_____
_____	_____	_____	_____
_____	_____	_____	_____
_____	_____	_____	_____
_____	_____	_____	_____
_____	_____	_____	_____
_____	_____	_____	_____
_____	_____	_____	_____
_____	_____	_____	_____
_____	_____	_____	_____

BOOK LIST

Name:_____ Date: _____

Title of Book: _____

Type of Book: _____

Author:_____ Date Read: _____

Comments: _____

_____

Other Books by this Author: _____

_____

Title of Book: _____

Type of Book: _____

Author:_____ Date Read: _____

Comments: _____

_____

Other Books by this Author: _____

_____

Title of Book: _____

Type of Book: _____

Author:_____ Date Read: _____

Comments: _____

_____

Other Books by this Author: _____

_____

FORM B110

HOBBIES AND INTERESTS

Name: _____

Hobby/Interest:_____

Associated Activities: _____

_____

_____

Other Relevant Information: _____

_____

Hobby/Interest:_____

Associated Activities: _____

_____

_____

Other Relevant Information: _____

_____

Hobby/Interest:_____

Associated Activities: _____

_____

_____

Other Relevant Information: _____

_____

Hobby/Interest:_____

Associated Activities: _____

_____

_____

Other Relevant Information: _____

_____

LIBRARY OF AUDIOCASSETTES

Name:_____ Date: _____

Item #	Title	Artist	Audio Type
_____	_____	_____	_____
_____	_____	_____	_____
_____	_____	_____	_____
_____	_____	_____	_____
_____	_____	_____	_____
_____	_____	_____	_____
_____	_____	_____	_____
_____	_____	_____	_____
_____	_____	_____	_____
_____	_____	_____	_____
_____	_____	_____	_____
_____	_____	_____	_____
_____	_____	_____	_____
_____	_____	_____	_____
_____	_____	_____	_____
_____	_____	_____	_____
_____	_____	_____	_____
_____	_____	_____	_____
_____	_____	_____	_____
_____	_____	_____	_____

Code for Audio Types: C = Cassette   CD = Compact Disc   R = Record

FORM L110

ROSTER OF SPORTING RESULTS

Name: _____

Sport: _____ Team: _____

Date	Rival Team	Location of Game	Score	Record to Date
_____	_____	_____	_____	_____
_____	_____	_____	_____	_____
_____	_____	_____	_____	_____
_____	_____	_____	_____	_____
_____	_____	_____	_____	_____
_____	_____	_____	_____	_____
_____	_____	_____	_____	_____
_____	_____	_____	_____	_____
_____	_____	_____	_____	_____
_____	_____	_____	_____	_____
_____	_____	_____	_____	_____
_____	_____	_____	_____	_____
_____	_____	_____	_____	_____
_____	_____	_____	_____	_____
_____	_____	_____	_____	_____
_____	_____	_____	_____	_____
_____	_____	_____	_____	_____
_____	_____	_____	_____	_____
_____	_____	_____	_____	_____
_____	_____	_____	_____	_____

TELEVISION VIEWING LOG

Name: _____

Week of: _____

	Time	Program	Channel	Hours
Sunday:	_____	_____	_____	_____
	_____	_____	_____	_____
	_____	_____	_____	_____
Monday:	_____	_____	_____	_____
	_____	_____	_____	_____
	_____	_____	_____	_____
Tuesday:	_____	_____	_____	_____
	_____	_____	_____	_____
	_____	_____	_____	_____
Wednesday	_____	_____	_____	_____
	_____	_____	_____	_____
	_____	_____	_____	_____
Thursday	_____	_____	_____	_____
	_____	_____	_____	_____
	_____	_____	_____	_____
Friday:	_____	_____	_____	_____
	_____	_____	_____	_____
	_____	_____	_____	_____
Saturday	_____	_____	_____	_____
	_____	_____	_____	_____
	_____	_____	_____	_____

Total Hours: _____

FORM T110

UPCOMING ENTERTAINMENT ATTRACTIONS

Name: _____

Month: _____ Year: _____

Event	Location	Date	Cost
Theatre:			
_____	_____	_____	$_____
_____	_____	_____	$_____
_____	_____	_____	$_____
Arts:			
_____	_____	_____	$_____
_____	_____	_____	$_____
_____	_____	_____	$_____
Movies:			
_____	_____	_____	$_____
_____	_____	_____	$_____
_____	_____	_____	$_____
Concerts:			
_____	_____	_____	$_____
_____	_____	_____	$_____
_____	_____	_____	$_____
Festivals/Fairs:			
_____	_____	_____	$_____
_____	_____	_____	$_____
_____	_____	_____	$_____
Specialty/Trade Shows:			
_____	_____	_____	$_____
_____	_____	_____	$_____
_____	_____	_____	$_____

VIDEOCASSETTE REGISTRY

Name:_____Date: _____

Tape #	Video Title	Type of Movie (comedy, etc.)	Running Time
_____	_____	_____	_____
_____	_____	_____	_____
_____	_____	_____	_____
_____	_____	_____	_____
_____	_____	_____	_____
_____	_____	_____	_____
_____	_____	_____	_____
_____	_____	_____	_____
_____	_____	_____	_____
_____	_____	_____	_____
_____	_____	_____	_____
_____	_____	_____	_____
_____	_____	_____	_____
_____	_____	_____	_____
_____	_____	_____	_____
_____	_____	_____	_____
_____	_____	_____	_____
_____	_____	_____	_____
_____	_____	_____	_____
_____	_____	_____	_____
_____	_____	_____	_____

FORM V110

VIDEOGAME COLLECTION

Name:_____Date: _____

Cartridge Name   Item #   Location

_____   _____   _____

_____   _____   _____

_____   _____   _____

_____   _____   _____

_____   _____   _____

_____   _____   _____

_____   _____   _____

_____   _____   _____

_____   _____   _____

_____   _____   _____

_____   _____   _____

_____   _____   _____

_____   _____   _____

_____   _____   _____

_____   _____   _____

_____   _____   _____

_____   _____   _____

_____   _____   _____

_____   _____   _____

_____   _____   _____

Section 11
Special Projects

Form A111   **Activity Planner - Monthly** – Helps you organize monthly projects

Form A211   **Activity Planner - Weekly** – Helps you organize weekly projects

Form M111   **Monthly Goals** – Lists goals planned for each month of the year

Form P111   **Personal Goals** – Divides your personal goals into certain time periods

Form P211   **Plans for Future Projects** – Lists ideas for future projects

Form P311   **Project Update** – Follow-up list on projects which have begun

Form S111   **Schedule of Projects** – Lists projected and actual project completion dates

Form S211   **Six-Month Goals** – Lists objectives and comments on planned six-month goals

Form T111   **Three-Month Goals** – Lists objectives and comments on planned three month goals

Form W111   **Weekly Objectives** – Lists goals to be completed each day of the week

ACTIVITY PLANNER - MONTHLY

Name: _____

Month of: _____ Year: _____

Date   Time   Activity

_____   _____   _____

_____   _____   _____

_____   _____   _____

_____   _____   _____

_____   _____   _____

_____   _____   _____

_____   _____   _____

_____   _____   _____

_____   _____   _____

_____   _____   _____

_____   _____   _____

_____   _____   _____

_____   _____   _____

_____   _____   _____

_____   _____   _____

_____   _____   _____

_____   _____   _____

_____   _____   _____

_____   _____   _____

_____   _____   _____

ACTIVITY PLANNER - WEEKLY

Name: _____

Week of: _____ Year: _____

Date   Time   Activity

_____   _____   _____

_____   _____   _____

_____   _____   _____

_____   _____   _____

_____   _____   _____

_____   _____   _____

_____   _____   _____

_____   _____   _____

_____   _____   _____

_____   _____   _____

_____   _____   _____

_____   _____   _____

_____   _____   _____

_____   _____   _____

_____   _____   _____

_____   _____   _____

_____   _____   _____

_____   _____   _____

_____   _____   _____

_____   _____   _____

FORM A211

MONTHLY GOALS

Name:_____ Year:_____

	Goal	Date to be Completed
January	_____	_____
	_____	_____
February	_____	_____
	_____	_____
March	_____	_____
	_____	_____
April	_____	_____
	_____	_____
May	_____	_____
	_____	_____
June	_____	_____
	_____	_____
July	_____	_____
	_____	_____
August	_____	_____
	_____	_____
September	_____	_____
	_____	_____
October	_____	_____
	_____	_____
November	_____	_____
	_____	_____
December	_____	_____
	_____	_____

PERSONAL GOALS

Name:_____ Date: _____

For Today: _____

_____

_____

_____

For this Week: _____

_____

_____

_____

For this Month: _____

_____

_____

_____

For this Year: _____

_____

_____

_____

To Accomplish within 5 Years: _____

_____

_____

To Accomplish within a Decade: _____

_____

_____

To Accomplish within a Lifetime: _____

_____

_____

FORM P111

PLANS FOR FUTURE PROJECTS

Name of Project Planner: _____

Date: _____

Project Concept:_____

Steps Taken to Date: _____

_____

Future Steps: _____

_____

Name of Project Planner: _____

Date: _____

Project Concept:_____

Steps Taken to Date: _____

_____

Future Steps: _____

_____

Name of Project Planner: _____

Date: _____

Project Concept:_____

Steps Taken to Date: _____

_____

Future Steps: _____

_____

PROJECT UPDATE

Name: _____

Type of Project: _____

Start Date: _____ Target Date: _____ Completed: _____

Steps Taken to Date: _____

_____

_____

Future Steps: _____

_____

_____

Comments/Suggestions: _____

_____

_____

Name: _____

Type of Project: _____

Start Date: _____ Target Date: _____ Completed: _____

Steps Taken to Date: _____

_____

_____

Future Steps: _____

_____

_____

Comments/Suggestions: _____

_____

_____

FORM P311

SCHEDULE OF PROJECTS

Name:_____ Date: _____

Project: _____
Estim. Completion Date: _____ Actual Completion Date: _____

Project: _____
Estim. Completion Date: _____ Actual Completion Date: _____

Project: _____
Estim. Completion Date: _____ Actual Completion Date: _____

Project: _____
Estim. Completion Date: _____ Actual Completion Date: _____

Project: _____
Estim. Completion Date: _____ Actual Completion Date: _____

Project: _____
Estim. Completion Date: _____ Actual Completion Date: _____

Project: _____
Estim. Completion Date: _____ Actual Completion Date: _____

Project: _____
Estim. Completion Date: _____ Actual Completion Date: _____

SIX-MONTH GOALS

Name:_____ Date: _____

Goal	Date Achieved	Comments
_____	_____	_____
_____	_____	_____
_____	_____	_____
_____	_____	_____
_____	_____	_____
_____	_____	_____
_____	_____	_____
_____	_____	_____
_____	_____	_____
_____	_____	_____
_____	_____	_____
_____	_____	_____
_____	_____	_____
_____	_____	_____
_____	_____	_____
_____	_____	_____
_____	_____	_____
_____	_____	_____
_____	_____	_____
_____	_____	_____

FORM S211

THREE-MONTH GOALS

Name:_____ Date: _____

Goal	Date Achieved	Comments
_____	_____	_____
_____	_____	_____
_____	_____	_____
_____	_____	_____
_____	_____	_____
_____	_____	_____
_____	_____	_____
_____	_____	_____
_____	_____	_____
_____	_____	_____
_____	_____	_____
_____	_____	_____
_____	_____	_____
_____	_____	_____
_____	_____	_____
_____	_____	_____
_____	_____	_____
_____	_____	_____
_____	_____	_____
_____	_____	_____

WEEKLY OBJECTIVES

Name:_____ Week of: _____

	Objective	Comments
Sunday:		

Sunday:

_____   _____

_____   _____

_____   _____

Monday:

_____   _____

_____   _____

_____   _____

Tuesday:

_____   _____

_____   _____

_____   _____

Wednesday:

_____   _____

_____   _____

_____   _____

Thursday:

_____   _____

_____   _____

_____   _____

Friday:

_____   _____

_____   _____

_____   _____

Saturday:

_____   _____

_____   _____

_____   _____

FORM W111

It's E·Z!
It's Family Record Organizer on disk!

N ow E·Z Legal Forms offers its Family Record Organizer in an easy-to-use **software program.**

Personal, legal and medical data with built-in math functions at your fingertips

◆ *Customize every form to suit your family needs.*

◆ *Print out accurate forms in minutes.*

◆ *Improve household record keeping and communication.*

ONLY **$49**⁹⁵ Order No. SW300
ISBN# 1-56382-003-X

Other E·Z Legal Forms®
Now Served Up To You
In PC-compatible
SOFTWARE

Legal forms in an easy-to-use, straightforward presentation. Programmed to run on a variety of PC platforms.

E·Z LEGAL SOFTWARE has been reviewed by lawyers and professional counsel to be sure all information is legally correct and in line with the laws governing your state. Look for E·Z LEGAL SOFTWARE programs wherever quality computer software is sold.

OPERATES UNDER WINDOWS

301 Legal Forms and Agreements

ONLY **$89**⁹⁵   Order No. SW301
ISBN# 1-56382-000-5

Personnel Director

ONLY **$79**⁹⁵   Order No. SW302
ISBN# 1-56382-004-8

Corporate Secretary

ONLY **$59**⁹⁵   Order No. SW304
ISBN# 1-56382-001-3

Credit Manager

ONLY **$59**⁹⁵   Order No. SW303
ISBN# 1-56382-002-1

All E·Z Legal Software includes 3 1/2" floppy disks, instruction manual and examples of every document. 5 1/4" disks available at no charge.

E·Z LEGAL® SOFTWARE
...when you need it in writing!™
301
Legal Forms and Agreements®

IRONCLAD LEGAL PROTECTION IN MINUTES!

• Legally protect yourself... your family... your property...

E·Z LEGAL® SOFTWARE
...when you need it in writing!™
PERSONNEL DIRECTOR®

AVOID EMPLOYER LIABILITY

IMPROVE EFFICIENCY & EMPLOYEE MORALE

Over 240 ready-to-use personnel agreements... forms... letters... and documents to manage your employees more efficiently, effectively... and legally!

• Vital for every size business

E·Z LEGAL® SOFTWARE
...when you need it in writing!™
CORPORATE SECRETARY®

INCLUDES FORMS TO INCORPORATE!

Now you can quickly and conveniently prepare and maintain your own up-to-date CORPORATE RECORDS... without a lawyer!

• Over 170 ready-to-use minutes, resolutions, notices and other

E·Z LEGAL® SOFTWARE
...when you need it in writing!™
CREDIT MANAGER

GET PAID! STOP CREDIT LOSSES!

A complete and proven credit and collection system of over 200 letters... agreements... notices... memos... and other documents to help you get paid ... EVERY TIME!

• Essential for every business that extends credit
• PC-compatible
• Save costly legal fees
• Valid in all 50 states

Other Essential BOOKS By E·Z Legal Forms

Get your business and your personal life in great form with E·Z Legal Books geared to your needs.

ONLY **$24**⁹⁵ each

301 Legal Forms and Agreements

A complete do-it-yourself library of 301 ready-to-use and simple-to-complete legal documents for virtually every personal or business situation.

Order No. BK301
ISBN 1-56382-301-2

Corporate Secretary

A complete corporate record organizer of over 170 minutes, resolutions, notices and other waivers to keep perfect corporate records without a lawyer!

Order No. BK304
ISBN 1-56382-304-7

Personnel Director

Over 240 ready-to-use personnel agreements... forms... letters... and documents to manage your employees more efficiently, effectively... and legally!

Order No. BK302
ISBN 1-56382-302-0

Credit Manager

Over 200 ready-to-use credit analyses, reports and logs to streamline your credit and billing systems.

Order No. BK303
ISBN 1-56382-303-9

ORDER FORM
for E·Z Legal books and software:

Total order is **$** _____ __*__ **for** ___ **items.**

*Florida residents add 6% sales tax.

- **Shipment is 4th class/book rate shipping.**
- **Add <u>$2 per item</u> for UPS or first-class postage.**
- **Canadian residents add <u>$1 per item.</u>**

---

1. Photocopy this order form.
2. Use the *photo copy* to complete your order and mail to:

> **E·Z Legal Forms, Inc.**
> **384 S. Military Trail**
> **Deerfield Beach, FL 33442**

CHECK OFF THE ITEMS YOU ARE ORDERING:

E·Z Legal Software

◇ 301 Legal Forms & Agreements	SW301	**$89.95**
◇ Personnel Director	SW302	**$79.95**
◇ Corporate Secretary	SW304	**$59.95**
◇ Credit Manager	SW303	**$59.95**
◇ Family Record Organizer	SW300	**$49.95**

E·Z Legal Books

◇ 301 Legal Forms & Agreements	BK301	**$24.95**
◇ Personnel Director	BK302	**$24.95**
◇ Corporate Secretary	BK304	**$24.95**
◇ Credit Manager	BK303	**$24.95**
◇ Family Record Organizer	BK300	**$24.95**

All prices are *suggested manufacturer's retail price* and subject to change without notice.

PAYMENT: If you are a government agency, college, library or other official public organization, include your P.O. # here:

Total payment must accompany all other orders.
(We cannot invoice individuals or private companies)

Make checks payable to: E·Z Legal Forms, Inc.

NAME _____

COMPANY/ORGANIZATION _____

ADDRESS _____

CITY _____ STATE ____ ZIP ____

PHONE: (_____) _____

PAYMENT: ☐ **CHECK ENCLOSED**

☐ **PLEASE CHARGE MY CREDIT CARD:**

☐ MasterCard ☐ VISA   EXP. DATE ☐☐☐☐

ACCOUNT. NO. ☐☐☐☐☐☐☐☐☐☐☐☐☐☐☐☐

Signature:_____
(required for credit card purchases)

– For faster service –

Order by phone:
(305) 480-8933

Fax your order:
(305) 480-8906